THE NATURE OF SOME OF OUR PHYSICAL CONCEPTS

THE NATURE OF SOME OF OUR PHYSICAL CONCEPTS

by P. W. BRIDGMAN

PHILOSOPHICAL LIBRARY
NEW YORK

LITHOGRAPHED IN THE UNITED STATES OF AMERICA

Introduction

The three lectures reprinted here were given in April 1950 under the auspices of the Department of the History and Philosophy of Science at City College, University of London, at the immediate invitation of Professor Herbert Dingle, Chairman of the Department. They were later published in the January, April, and August 1951 numbers of the British Journal for the Philosophy of Science. I am much indebted to the editor of the Journal, Dr. G. C. Crombie, and to the publishers, Thomas Nelson and Sons of Edinburgh, for generous permission to reprint in book form.

In these lectures I have attempted a more articulate analysis than hitherto of the operations involved in some of our physical concepts, particularly an analysis of the operations into their instrumental and their "paper and pencil" and verbal components. I have been becoming increasingly appreciative of the importance of the role which our verbal demands play, not only in the structure of our formal theories, but also as a tool capable of suggesting new experiments. There is a constant reaction, back and forth, between the instrumental and the verbal aspects of our operations.

In the first lecture I discuss the general operational approach in as much detail as needed for immediate purposes. Some of the consequences with regard to the field concept, the concept of empty space, and the nature of light are then developed in fuller detail than formerly in my Logic of Modern Physics. The second and third lectures are devoted more explicitly to an analysis of the reaction back and forth of the instrumental and verbal aspects of our operations. The subject of the analysis has been taken from my two books: The Nature of Thermodynamics, and the Thermodynamics of Electrical Phenomena in Metals. In these books I had tried to show that some of our conventional concepts require extension. For instance, the complete localization of both energy and entropy has to be recognized, with corresponding fluxes and a "creation function" for entropy. In describing electrical phenomena in massive conductors the conventional picture of an electromotive force driving the current is not adequate, but the conventional electromotive force must be recognized to have two aspects, not at all equivalent in the general case, although equivalent in elementary situations. We are forced to recognize unfamiliar aspects of the electric current, such as the convection by it of thermal energy. In these lectures I trace in detail how our verbal demands force us to extend these old concepts in a manner essentially unique, and how these extended concepts then demand new experimental effects, which are checked with experiment.

The analysis which I here present of the way in which our verbal demands force these extensions of concepts is a much more self conscious analysis than I made in the two books in which I first extended the concepts. In the books it merely appeared to me that my argument had a certain inevitability, without much reflection on my part as to how it was that I had a right to argue at all. I am here seeing what I did in a new light. This, on a small scale, is typical I think of what has often happened in physics on a grander scale. It is the practise that comes first—we find how to deal with a situation, and then reflection after the event puts the practise in a new light. However, even our most sophisticated reflection after the event will not, I think, completely dispel our wonder at the wisdom of our practise or our wonder that our verbal edifice meshes as coherently as it does with its foudations in practise.

P. W. BRIDGMAN

THE NATURE OF SOME OF OUR PHYSICAL CONCEPTS

I

In these lectures we shall try to develop an awareness of the operational content of several of the important concepts of physics. The profitableness of such an operational awareness was perhaps first forced on the attention of physicists by the special theory of relativity of Einstein and later by quantum mechanics. I believe that there are still unexplored implications in the macroscopic concepts of classical physics, and that our understanding of some of these concepts and our method of handling them is not even yet satisfactory in all respects. We shall attempt here to study some of the implications of pushing our operational analysis further than is customary.

The fundamental idea back of an operational analysis is simple enough ; namely that we do not know the meaning of a concept unless we can specify the operations which were used by us or our neighbour in applying the concept in any concrete situation. If we can thus specify the operations we can to a large extent reproduce the situation which was encountered by us or our neighbour and which we are trying to communicate. The operational aspect is not by any means the only aspect of meaning, but it is often the most important single aspect, particularly in scientific situations and in a society with as homogeneous a background as ours. In making an operational analysis we are dealing with necessary, as distinguished from sufficient, conditions. I have already expounded in several writings [1] various consequences of the operational point of view, so that only a comparatively brief indication of what is involved is necessary here. In this analysis the concept of operation is itself accepted as unanalysed. It is a matter of experience that we can perform certain operations at will, and that our neighbour can perform the ' same ' operations. Operations have a certain repeatability and identifiability and therefore ' objectivity ' ; this we take as a matter of observation and do not inquire how it comes about that this is true.

The operations which are important in the formation of the concepts of physics, or of science in general, may be of different kinds. In the first place there are the operations of the laboratory, or instrumental operations, in many cases operations of measurement. The sense organs are here to be considered as instruments. It was in an analysis of the instrumental operations of measuring lengths and times that Einstein discovered those overlooked features that are the basis of special relativity, and the present operational attitude of many physicists toward the concepts of physics largely stems from this analysis of Einstein. It is often supposed that the operational criterion of meaning demands that the operations which give meaning to a physical concept *must* be instrumental operations. This is, I believe, palpably a mistaken point of view, for simple observation shows that physicists do profitably employ concepts the meaning of which is not to be found in the instrumental operations of the laboratory, and which cannot be reduced to such operations without residue. Nearly all the concepts of theoretical or mathematical physics are of this character, such for example as the stress inside an elastic body subject to surface forces, or the ψ function of wave mechanics. In fact, there is hardly any physical concept which does not enter to a certain extent into some theoretical edifice and which does not therefore possess to a certain degree a non-instrumental component. All these non-instrumental operations we may loosely lump together as ' mental ' operations. Among the many mental operations we may single out for special attention the sort of operations performed by the theoretical physicist in his mathematical manipulations and characterise these as ' paper-and-pencil ' operations. Among the paper-and-pencil operations are to be included all manipulations with symbols, whether or not the symbols are the conventional symbols of mathematics.

[1] *The Logic of Modern Physics*, New York, 1927 ; *The Nature of Physical Theory*, Princeton, 1936 ; several chapters in *Reflections of a Physicist*, New York, 1950.

It will usually be sufficient to recognise only these two kinds of operations, namely instrumental and paper-and-pencil operations. Sometimes, however, it will be profitable to recognise other sorts of mental operation than the pencil-and-paper operation, although the line of separation is by no means sharp. Probably the most important of these are the verbal operations. Civilised man lives to a large extent in a verbal world of his own making : in this verbal world he exhibits patterns of behaviour which he finds no less compelling than the patterns forced on him by the 'external' objects of the physical world. He can make verbal experiments, as by asking himself ' would I say thus and thus in such and such a situation ?' The sort of physical concept which he finds it profitable or at least congenial to use is usually determined to a certain extent by his verbal demands as disclosed by such verbal experiments. The formal element or the element of pure construction in our physical concepts is often determined by such verbal demands. In our analysis we shall recognise several situations in which the demands of our verbalisation have been effectively directive.

Not only do we make verbal experiments, but we also make experiments in connection with the paper-and-pencil component of our operations. These are often referred to as ' mental ' experiments, without other qualification, although strictly a verbal experiment must also be recognised as ' mental.' The conventional mental experiment of the physicist is a highly idealised experiment with conceptualised physical instruments, ignoring in many cases physical limitations which in principle would make the experiment impossible. For example, in the classical electron theory of Lorentz, a meaning was given to the electrostatic force at points inside the electron in terms of the same conceptual operations which give meaning to the ordinary macroscopic electrostatic field, ignoring the essential physical fact that no charge smaller than an electron exists to serve as the test body in determining and giving meaning to the field. It will be found, I think, that in many of the situations of theoretical physics our meanings are to be sought in terms of mental experiments of this sort. This is, however, by no means the case in all the situations of theoretical physics, but particularly in the abstract situations of wave mechanics we are content to do without the visualisation afforded by the mental experiment and utilise only the paper-and-pencil operations of mathematical symbolistion.

The paper-and-pencil world is a world in which free invention is

9

possible, divorced from any immediate contact with the instrumental world of the laboratory. In this world of free invention discoveries are possible just as in the laboratory. The matter of nomenclature is not important here—we discover that we can invent. In this world we demand of ourselves that we be able to answer any question in which we can discover a meaning and that we be able to foretell the outcome of any describable mental experiment. Discovering a meaning in questions asked by analogy is one of the methods of discovery, for meanings so discovered may then suggest new experiments in the instrumental world.

It will be seen that a very great latitude is allowed to the verbal and the paper-and-pencil operation. I think, however, that physicists are agreed in imposing one restriction on the freedom of such operations, namely that such operations must be capable of eventually, although perhaps indirectly, making connection with instrumental operations. Only in this way can the physicist keep his feet on the ground or achieve a satisfactory degree of precision ; instrumental contact affords the only ' reality ' which he accepts as pertinent for him. Doubtless concepts which are not capable of eventual instrumental emergence but which are permanently confined to the verbal domain, like many of those used in daily life, are of the greatest importance in affecting human behaviour. Politics, philosophy and religion are full of such purely verbal concepts ; it is merely that such concepts are outside the field of the physicist.

The most important of our paper-and-pencil operations, as already suggested, are doubtless those which we perform when we mathematicise. There are two points to be considered here : the nature of the mathematical operations themselves, and the nature of the step by which we transport ourselves from the universe of instrumental operations to the universe of the operations of mathematics. It is in the first place obvious that mathematical operations are by nature different, in at least one important respect, from the instrumental operations of the laboratory. The latter are always subject to a certain haziness or margin of error, as when we try to push our readings to the limit by estimating the fraction of the smallest division of our instrument. There is no such haziness in mathematics, but any number may be written out to an unlimited number of decimal places (by repetition of zeroes in any event), far beyond the possible precision of any physical measurement. Furthermore, the numbers thus specified by mathematics yield by mathematical manipulation other numbers also perfectly sharp, subject to no instrumental or psychological uncertainty, and corresponding to nothing we encounter in physical experience. For instance, the statement of geometry that the length of a straight line connecting two points is less than that of any other joining line, no matter how little it may deviate from the straight line, corresponds to no statement that we are in a position to verify about our actual experience. Such sharpness does not reproduce the structure of experience, and in this respect mathematics fails, if indeed it is the object of mathematics to reproduce this aspect of experience. But it is often stated that the world around us is essentially mathematical in nature and is controlled by laws of mathematical precision. It seems to me that this view cannot be maintained, and that the correspondence with the world of mathematics is not a complete correspondence. When dealing with mathematics we are in a different world from the world of the laboratory. In mathematics we are dealing with paper-and-pencil operations which are palpably our own invention. Although mathematics is an invention, it is obviously a good invention, for only by means of it have we been able to acquire the degree of understanding and control of nature which we now enjoy.

In applying the invention of mathematics to the world about us we are forced to make a logical jump, for which I think there can be no rigorous justification. When we theorise about the results of a measurement, we replace the results of the measurements, with all their inevitable haziness, with mathematically sharp numbers. Just which one of the infinitely many mathematical numbers which would correspond to the measurement within its margin of error we select is entirely undetermined by any logical criterion. The choice is made by some quite extraneous consideration, such as simplicity or ease of manipulation. We do not ordinarily regard it as necessary to justify our choice, and fortify ourselves in our indifference by our extensive past experience which has shown it to be a matter of little moment.

Our discussion up to this point has been on a level where we can treat mathematics and logic as sharp. But it is possible to push the analysis to another level at which their sharpness disappears, the level at which we see mathematics and logic as human activities subject to the haziness of all such enterprise and containing an experimental component. It is not possible to ply the enterprise of logic without the concepts of identity and recurrence—we must be able to assure ourselves that we are making the *same* proposition *twice*, and in giving ourselves this assurance the haze enters.

11

If mathematics and logic are not perfectly sharp and contain an experimental component, what validity in the instrumental world does a conclusion have which has been reached by mathematical or logical analysis? Is it superfluous to verify a conclusion reached in this way? To make the question specific, suppose that we have established by experiment that the equation $\dfrac{d^2s}{dt^2} = g$ describes the motion of any freely falling body. We then deduce from this equation by the logical steps of mathematics that the distance fallen by any body starting from rest is connected with the time of fall by the equation $s = \frac{1}{2}\,gt^2$. Is it superfluous to verify this result by measurement? I think a common answer could be that verification is quite superfluous, on the ground that the integrated form of the equation is already implied (whatever 'implied' may mean) in the differential equation from which we started. I think a better answer would be that the answer depends on the physical operations which we have chosen to employ for our verification, first of the differential equation, and then of the integrated form. If the operations for these two verifications are such that both verifications may be made from the same set of readings in a note book, then we may say that verification of the integrated equation is superfluous except in so far as it guards against our own blunders. But if the set of readings made to verify the differential equation is not the same as made to verify the integrated equation, then verification is not superfluous. The experimental situation may be treated from either point of view. We might, for example, verify the differential equation from closely spaced readings of position and time, recorded perhaps with a high speed movie camera, the position being given by the readings on a long continuously graduated scale over which the body falls, and the time by the position of the hands of a clock carried with the falling body. In this case the identical set of readings would be used to verify the two equations, and verification may be said to be superfluous and tautological. We would also obtain verification in this case if the scale were graduated in any arbitrary non-uniform way, and the motion of the body were so manipulated by invisible strings as to satisfy the integrated equation.

In setting up the system in this way, with a long stationary scale and a falling clock, we have done more than is required for a verification of the differential equation. To do this it would be adequate to distribute along the path of the falling body a series of infinitesimal measuring sticks and, beside each infinitesimal stick, a clock adjusted to the correct rate but with an arbitrary zero setting. With this set-up, we could verify the differential equation, but not the integrated form. Verification is not now superfluous, but involves a check on whether the origins of the various infinitesimal measuring sticks have been so adjusted that $s = \int ds$, and the settings of the various clocks so adjusted that $t = \int dt$. (This discussion has obviously not been concerned with relativity considerations.)

It is possible to adopt an extreme view here and maintain that in no case is verification tautological or superfluous. This is the point of view of extreme sophistication which sees our whole conceptual method of handling the world, our recognition of objects with identity and our logical methods of handling them, as merely, at any epoch of time, a summary of past experience up to that date, with no guarantee of continuance and therefore with continual need of verification. I can see no logical method of refuting this position and I think it is essentially correct, but it is obvious that the physicist, or any one else for that matter, must operate on a different level to get anywhere.

We need not take as extreme a position as this to maintain that verification in this particular case is not superfluous, or in any other case where the mathematics has presented us with an integrated equation out of a differential equation. I think that many of the contemporaries of Newton or Leibnitz would have keenly felt the need of an experimental verification of the possibility of representing any actual situation by a differential equation. For the concepts for dealing with motion are not easily derived from the concepts with which static situations may be successfully handled, nor is the concept of a mathematical limit easy or its connection obvious with what we do in the laboratory. It must have been many years before our present mental serenity was acquired in the face of the operations of the calculus. It is perhaps possible even today to take the position that a differential equation is entirely an affair of the paper-and-pencil domain and therefore can never be subject to instrumental verification. I prefer to take what is perhaps a less rigorous point of view, and handle a differential equation, in such situations as that of the falling body, as something of which it makes sense to ask ' is it true ? ' It is, I think, in any event obvious that a ' law of nature,' or merely the results of specific observations, when embodied in differential form, of necessity contains a larger paper-and-pencil component than when expressed in integrated form. There is no physical operation corresponding exactly to the mathematical operation of taking the limit. What happens in the physical situation is perhaps sufficiently suggested by our description above of a verification of the differential equation of a falling body in terms of closely spaced photographs with a high speed movie camera. In general, we make our instrumental readings as closely spaced as we can, and then make a logical jump to the paper-and-pencil domain by plotting these readings on paper on a greatly magnified scale and observing that we can draw a smooth curve through them. We regard the differential equation as verified if we can detect no consistent discrepancy between the smooth curve which we draw so as to satisfy the equation and the plotted experimental points. There is never any question of proceeding to a limit in the mathematical sense, and logically the hiatus between the paper-and-pencil operations of the calculus and our instrumental operations cannot be closed. We do not regard this hiatus as particularly serious, however, and think of a law of nature when formulated in differential form as something of which it has meaning to say that it may be directly verified.

Perhaps we have been making too much of the logical hiatus between the differential equation and the results of instrumental operations, because we have already seen that even when we express our results in integrated form there is of necessity a logical hiatus in that no instrumental result has the sharpness of a number in mathematics. It is merely that the failure of logical correspondence is perhaps somewhat aggravated in the case of the differential equation.

We now turn to a detailed analysis of some of our specific physical concepts. We shall particularly attempt to separate the instrumental from the paper-and-pencil or verbal component, and to see in just what way the paper-and-pencil or verbal component makes its eventual instrumental contact.

The first of the concepts to which we direct ourselves is the concept of the ' field.' The concept of the field is often presented as one of the cornerstones of modern physics, invented by the intuitional genius of Faraday, clothed in mathematical form by Maxwell, and crowned by Einstein in his general relativity theory. The great virtue of the field concept is usually stated to be that it absolves us from accepting that intellectual monstrosity, action at a distance. It is felt to be more acceptable to rational thought to conceive of the gravitational action of the sun on the earth, for example, as propagated through the intermediate space by the handing on of some sort of influence from one point to its proximate neighbour, than to think of the action overleaping the intervening distance and finding its target by some sort of teleological clairvoyance. That is, the intermediate space is pictured as the seat of some sort of physical action which propagates itself from point to point, eventually concentrating itself on its target, where it manifests itself in the form of a mechanical force. Now if this concept of something going on in apparently empty space is to be capable of eventual instrumental emergence and thus to have physical content, there must be some instrumental method of demonstrating that there is something going on. There seems to be only one conceivable method of demonstrating such a state of affairs, and that is to go to the point in question with a suitable instrument and observe that the instrument gives a reading. This we can in fact do. For our instrument we may use a small massive particle attached to a spring balance, and when we transport our instrument to the point in question the spring balance gives a reading, which by varying the orientation of the balance may be converted into a reading of a vector 'force' acting on the particle. Our point of view is therefore thus far justified. But have we really done what by implication we set out to do, and shown that the other point of view, of action at a distance, is inadmissable? Would not our instrument still give exactly the same reading as before if we had action at a distance? I think it is obvious that it would, and that as far as the instrumental criterion goes there is no distinction. This dilemma seems to be unconsciously recognised, and apparently resolved to general satisfaction, by defining the field at a point, not as the force acting on the actual exploring particle, but as something derived from the measured force, namely the limit of the ratio of the force to the exploring mass as the mass becomes smaller without limit. The limiting ratio obtained in this way is defined as the 'field' at the point, and is conceptualised as something characterising the point by itself, from which the effect of the test mass has disappeared because its magnitude has vanished. This is, it seems to me, plainly not a correct way of conceptualising the result of going to the limit, for the physical effect of the test mass persists throughout every stage of the limiting process, the force on the mass finally vanishing together with the mass. The effect of the mass has in nowise disappeared in the limit, since we are taking a ratio of two quantities, both approaching zero. The device of taking the limit thus appears as unsuccessful in accomplishing the desired purpose.

15

There is, of course, a legitimate reason for using the limiting process in defining the field at a *point* ; the limit may be necessary to smooth out the effect of space variations of the field if the field varies rapidly from point to point and the test mass extends over a region wide enough so that the variation is perceptible. Also the limiting process is necessary to eliminate the reaction of the exploring instrument back on the distribution which gives rise to the field ; this remark is particularly applicable when the field is an electric field arising from a distribution of charge on conductors.

Furthermore, a serious logical difficulty appears when the field concept is carried through in mathematical detail. For it appears that the *mechanism* by which the field exerts a force on the charge is by way of the perturbations which the test charge automatically introduces in the field. These perturbations are the essence of the matter because they are proportional to the test charge and account for the entire force. Thus even in the paper-and-pencil domain of mathematical manipulation we can find no operational meaning in terms of mental experiments of a field undisturbed by the instrument of measurement.

It seems to me that there is no way by which the desired distinction between action at a distance and action by a field can be given instrumental significance. For always the instrument by which we would establish the existence of the field is subject to the suspect action at a distance. The situation which has thus presented itself is part of a more general situation, for always, from the point of view of operations, it is fruitless and meaningless to attempt to establish the existence of anything independent of the means by which its existence is established or verified. The two together, object and means of observation or measurement, form an indissoluble union ; either without the other is meaningless, at least in the instrumental domain. Yet from the point of view of common sense it is incontestable that we do conceptualise the objects of daily life as having an existence independent of the instrument or method of observation. In the commonsense domain the meaning of this is clear enough ; it is that we are able to adapt ourselves to everyday objects, that is, to draw our programmes of action involving the objects, without taking explicit account in those programmes of the methods by which we acquired our knowledge. Since the method of observation is irrelevant for our usual purposes, it is economy of thought to forget it, and we think of objects as having an existence independent of observation.

This commonsense view comes to colour all our thinking and we carry it over uncritically into situations not sufficiently like those of common sense to justify the extension.

Returning now to our analysis of the field concept, ostensibly the device of making our exploring charge vanishingly small in the limit provides the means of achieving independence of the measuring process, but actually, as we have seen, it does not, the presence of the charge itself, even when vanishingly small, always being an essential element in the situation. The situation might conceivably be improved if there were *two* or more independent instrumental means of verifying the existence of the field, such for example as the electrostatic double refraction which accompanies an electrostatic field in a transparent body. But apparently there are not two such independent instrumental approaches in empty space, but the only instrumental meaning of the field is in terms of the force on test bodies. Such other effects as double refraction occur only in the presence of matter, which automatically provides the possibility of action by contiguous contact. But even if there were two or more independent means of demonstrating the existence of a field, it is not at all obvious that we could then show that action at a distance is not an alternative method of description.

Although we apparently cannot have two independent instrumental methods of directly verifying the existence of the field or showing the impossibility of action at a distance, there may be other sorts of phenomena and other sorts of instrumentation that may, in a wider setting, make the field concept under certain circumstances so much more convenient to handle than that of action at a distance that we may use it exclusively. Such independent phenomena do exist in the case of the electromagnetic field, so that the whole picture is different for electrical than for gravitational phenomena. We will return to this question in connection with the concept of energy and its localisation.

However repulsive the concept of action at a distance may be to our mechanical intuition, it does not violate the broadest demand which we can put on the sort of account we must give of the external world if we are eventually to reduce the external world to understandability. It seems to me that the broadest basis on which we can hope for an eventual understanding is *invariable correlation between the results of instrumental operations.* Given invariable correlation, we can find how to predict, and prediction is perhaps the most searching criterion of understanding. We can have such invariable correlation either in terms of a field or of action at a distance.

The fundamental situation with which we are confronted here and the demands which we automatically exact of our treatment of the situation come perilously close to involving an inner contradiction. We want to talk about a field in otherwise empty space, and we demand that we have some instrumental indication of the existence of the field in spite of, or ignoring, the fact that the space can no longer be empty when we introduce the instrument of detection. The failure of the space to be empty in the presence of the detecting instrument is not an irrelevant effect that can be neglected, for how shall we rule out the possibility that the detecting instrument has introduced something with it, indissolubly tethered to it, like the physical lines of force of J. J. Thomson? To deduce an objectively existing field from instrumental measurements of a force which is proportional to the test charge involves the same sort of situation as if in the ordinary realm of macroscopic phenomena the mass of a body were proportional to the intensity of the light with which we observe it. The concept of independently existing objects certainly would not have formed itself under such conditions. So here, it is only by an uncritical analogy that we form the concept of a field independently existing in its own right. Apparently all that nature will grant us here is the instrumental reaction when we station our instrument at any point in formerly unoccupied space; she will not grant us the further right to analyse our experience into a field as distinguished from action at a distance. Instrumentally the distinction between field and action at a distance appears to be meaningless. We must accordingly recognise that the distinction which physicists actually do make between these two concepts is verbal, and the corresponding operations are verbal operations. There is no doubt that verbalisations about the distinction between the field and the action at·a distance points of view have played an important part in the activity of physicists, as may be seen by consulting the literature. Doubtless with our present mathematical machinery it is much more convenient, particularly when dealing with electromagnetic phenomena, to prefer the field to the action at a distance point of view, but one may feel a certain scepticism as to whether such distinctions really play an essential role.

We have been talking about ' empty ' space in connection with the field concept. In the concept of 'empty' space we are again coming perilously close to an inner contradiction. For how shall we establish that a purportedly empty space is really empty without going there with an instrument to prove it, and when we have introduced the instrument the space is no longer empty. In the realm of macroscopic experience with ordinary matter we can deal with similar situations by setting up a theory which takes account of the effect of the instrument so that we can correct for the perturbations introduced by the instrument, as when we correct for the effect of the size of the bulb of a thermometer on temperature readings. The theory by which we correct for the perturbations is based on the variation in the behaviour of the instrument when it is applied to a range of situations. But in the limit when the matter vanishes but the instrument does not, such procedure fails us, while the intellectual compulsion remains to give some instrumental meaning to the purported emptiness of space. The simplest way of meeting this compulsion is simply to say that the space is empty if *no* instrument gives any reading when introduced into it. But are there such empty spaces ? Up to a short time ago it would have been accepted as intuitively obvious that it was permissible to use the concept of empty space in our speculating with no danger of ever encountering inner contradiction. In fact, the concept of empty space seemed almost a necessity of thought. A sufficiently critical insight might have seen, however, that the question of the 'real existence' of empty space was in some way bound up with the behaviour of instruments, and so became a question of experiment rather than of *a priori* logic. And now within the last few years we have the quantum mechanical concept of a fluctuating zero point electrostatic field in otherwise empty space. If the theory is correct, it means that it will be found as a matter of experiment that it never occurs that there are places where all physical instruments give no readings, so that 'empty' space corresponds as little to the physical actuality as do the simultaneous position and momentum prohibited by the Heisenberg principle of interdetermination. In this denial of the legitimateness of the concept of empty space it seems to me that we have as dramatic a demonstration as can be imagined of the impossibility of divorcing our concepts from the operations by which they are generated and of the impossibility of speaking of things existing of themselves in their own right.

There is another class of physical phenomena in which we form our concepts by ignoring part of the operational background, namely the phenomena of the propagation of light or radiation in general. There have been a number of different physical pictures of the nature of light, all of which have had the feature in common that light is to be regarded as in some way a ' thing travelling.' This statement obviously is applicable to the old corpuscular theory of light ; it is true for the electromagnetic theory where the ' thing ' is a phase in the electromagnetic field, which may be followed in thought as it moves, as in Einstein's special relativity ; or finally we have the ' thing travelling' picture in the photons of quantum mechanics. What instrumental method shall we adopt to show that when we have light we also have a thing travelling ? In the realm of ordinary optical phenomena we are here confronted with the same sort of self-defeating requirement that we have already met in trying to distinguish instrumentally between the field and action at a distance or in trying to give instrumental meaning to empty space. For the only method of detecting the presence of light is to put a screen in the path of the radiation and observe that the screen is illuminated. We never experience light as such but only things lighted ; operationally, light means things lighted and not a thing travelling. Any meaning that can be given to the thing travelling concept can be only an indirect meaning, involving other sorts of operation than those contained in the definition. What other sorts of operation would be acceptable ? In the case of ordinary travelling things, such as a baseball in flight from pitcher to catcher, there are other phenomena besides those at the delivering and receiving ends, such as being able to see the ball in flight or detecting the wind as it passes. But we cannot see a photon in flight nor does it create a wind. All that we have is certain geometrical relations between things lighted which are the same as if there were rectilinear propagation (neglecting here diffraction and similar effects). There is, however, no instrumental method of proving that ' action at a distance ' does not also follow rectilinear rules. I believe that the situation is not altered by considering the *velocity* of light, for there appears to be no reason in principle why action at a distance should not take place at more distant points at later instants of time, thus involving the instrumental attributes of a velocity of propagation. Until new sorts of experimental fact are discovered it seems to me that the concept of light as a thing travelling remains a predominantly paper-and-pencil concept, mostly verbal in character. This verbal concept is of undoubted value because it enables us to make our mental experiments and conduct our paper-and-pencil operations in a congenial fashion closely analogous to the way in which we treat ordinary material macroscopic objects. But I doubt whether there is any logical necessity here, and I believe that all the results could also be obtained with a theoretical apparatus that pictured light as some sort of delayed action at a distance.

The proviso above ' until new sorts of experimental fact are discovered ' is an essential part of the situation, and indicates that purely verbal concepts may nevertheless have instrumental implications and therefore not be indifferently equivalent to each other if we consider them in the context of the programmes of experiment which they suggest. The application here is immediate. For if light ' really ' consists of photons travelling and these photons have physical ' existence ' then we would anticipate some sort of interference between the photons of two beams of light crossing each other in otherwise empty space. Theory should be in a position to calculate the amount of such interference to be expected. The calculations have been made and it proves that the amount of interference to be expected is too small to be detectable with light intensities at present attainable. If and when such interference effects can be instrumentally detected the concept of light as a thing travelling will have been so far justified.

There is another way of dealing with light which is closely related to the thing-travelling point of view, namely to speak of light as going *through* space. Again we meet a self-defeating situation, for any instrument set to detect the passage of light by its very presence prevents the passage. Instrumentally, light only departs and arrives. The emphasis in speaking of light going through space is different from the emphasis in speaking of a thing travelling, for now we direct attention to the space, and presently are speaking of a *propagation* of light through space, and of space having the *property* of propagating light with a definite velocity. At first glance it is as paradoxical to assign properties to empty space as it was a few pages back to discover that no instrumental meaning can be given to empty space. The two points of view now appear merely as two aspects of a wider vision, namely that since what we shall find by instrumental manipulation is wholly a matter for experiment to decide, we cannot have unlicensed freedom in our paper-and-pencil concepts if we also demand that our paper-and-pencil concepts eventually emerge into the instrumental world.

Formally, and taken in isolation, the point of view of light as a thing travelling or propagated cannot be justified in preference to the point of view of light as a thing departing and arriving with retardation in time, so that whichever point of view is adopted it must be described as a convention. It may well be, however, that one of two alternative points of view is so much more congenial to the commonsense way of looking at things, the commonsense point of view itself being recognised as at bottom a construction, that we shall adopt it in preference to the other. It may well happen that in an early stage of knowledge there was little to choose between two points of view but with the discovery of new experimental facts the convenience and simplicity of one point of view comes to be so overwhelming as to result in the unanimous discarding of the other. This is what happened with our concepts of atoms. Fifty years ago there was a serious school led by Ostwald, that maintained that the concept of atoms was superfluous, since all it expressed was the fact of constant combining weights in chemistry. But with all our new experimental discoveries, the implications of Brownian motion and tracks in a Wilson condensation chamber, to mention only two, the convenience of the atomic picture has become so overwhelming that we have discarded the alternative point of view completely, and speak of the situation in different terms, as when it is often stated that all these facts have proved the *reality* of atoms. I suspect, however, that the logical situation has been in no way altered by all the new experimental discoveries, and that the old Ostwald point of view could be carried through if we were willing to pay the price in complexity. (Incidentally, this example suggests what the operational meaning of *reality* is.) It seems to me that very much the same sort of thing that happened with regard to our concept of atoms is now happening with regard to our concepts of light and field and empty space and action at a distance. With the discovery of new facts, such as the creation of electron pairs in apparently empty space, the one point of view becomes so much more convenient that we forget the possibility of the other and discard it. But I think we should not forget what we are doing here and remember that logically we have nothing unique but are adopting a particular convention because of the naturalness with which it enters our commonsense scheme of thought.

II

In this second lecture we shall examine some of the concepts of thermodynamics. We shall be especially concerned to separate the instrumental from the paper-and-pencil component of the operations that define these concepts. It will appear that the paper-and-pencil operations have to satisfy certain demands which in their turn react on the instrumental operations, with the result that in the final picture the instrumental operations have a greater generality than in the original picture.

Let us begin by considering the first law of thermodynamics as conventionally formulated :

$$dE = dQ + dW$$

By choosing to write the law in differential form we have already injected a strong paper-and-pencil component into the situation. This aspect is, however, not of particular importance for our present purposes and has already been sufficiently discussed in the first lecture. We shall be here concerned with other implications. Writing the law in this form implies in the first place that the universe has been divided into two parts : the 'system,' to which the law as written applies, and the rest of the universe, 'external' to the system. 'External' need not be, although it usually is, taken in the sense of geometrically external. In the equation as thus applied, dE is the change of internal energy of the system in any interval of time, dQ is the heat received by the system and dW the mechanical energy or 'work' received by the system from outside, both during the same time interval. If the equation had its ostensible significance, it would mean that dE, dQ, and dW are all to be determined by independent instrumental operations, and that then it will be found as a matter of experiment that the equality written holds. But this is not the actual meaning, for there is no instrumental operation by which dE may be determined which can be formulated so as to apply universally in all situations. The equation as it stands defines dE, it being assumed that dQ and dW are obtainable independently by suitable instrumental operations. The equation, however, is more than a definition of dE; it acquires physical content through the statement appended to the equation that dE so defined is a perfect differential in the variables that fix the state of the system, although dW and dQ taken separately are not such perfect differentials. The concept of 'state' itself is assumed to be already formed, and the variables which determine the state must be known by independent experiment before thermodynamics is applied. What we mean by the 'state' of a system is the complex of all its measurable properties. A state is fixed by its appropriate variables in the sense that whenever the variables resume their former values, the body is again in its former state as determined by all its measurable properties. It is usually understood that the state variables are obtained by measurements made 'now,' that is, that the state variables are not affected by the history of the system. This restriction may, however, be partially lifted in certain special cases, as in a body which is traversing repeatable cycles of hysteresis.

From the fact that dE is a perfect differential, the conservation properties of energy, or more properly, change of energy, follow by conventional lines of argument. Application of the equation to any concrete instance can give only the value of the integral of dE from an initial to a final state, that is, a change of energy. Although no general lines of procedure can be laid down by which the change of energy can be obtained in the general case, except through the definition, nevertheless, for every specific concrete system it is possible to give rules by which the change of energy may be found in terms only of the state variables by a suitable combination of instrumental and calculational procedures. These procedures require rehearsal and previous measurement on the specific system, but do not involve an application of thermodynamics. For instance, if the system is an ordinary p-t-v system, then the previous measurements involve a determination of the characteristic equation of the substance and the heat absorbed along some non-isothermal. If the system involves a magnetic field, then a determination of energy will demand measurements of magnetic permeability and of magnetic field strength. No case is known which does not fit into the picture, for it has been possible to devise appropriate procedures to fit every extension to new types of force. This fact has led to a view of the nature of energy which is associated most closely perhaps with the name of Poincaré. According to this view, energy is most appropriately described as a convention, made to suit our convenience, but with no further significance.

Poincaré's argument for this is that if we were ever confronted by a situation in which the conservation of energy apparently failed, we would at once save the situation by inventing a new form of energy. The justification for this point of view is implied in the discussion just given. I believe, however, that this is only a very partial picture and that energy is far more than a mere convention. For after we have invented the new form of energy to meet some specific new situation, it is required that this new form of energy be applicable to all the other situations in which we now find that the new energy appears. For instance, the newly formulated magnetic energy must be applicable in every situation in which a magnetic force appears. But much more than this, there are reciprocal relations involving the new energy and the entire previous thermodynamic universe of discourse before the new energy was recognised. For instance, when magnetic energy is recognised as a new form of energy, we find that thermodynamics demands a relation between the effect of pressure on magnetic permeability and the magnetostrictive change of volume when a substance is exposed to a magnetic field, a relation which is subject to independent experimental confirmation. Taken in its entirety, energy and its conservation are much more than a convention and express a relationship which is in our control only to a trivial extent. And since there is no general instrumental method of measuring or defining energy, but each new kind of situation has to be met by new *ad hoc* invention, it follows that the discovery of each new kind of force constitutes a new crisis from the point of view of the energy concept, the outcome of which is uncertain until the appropriate invention has been discovered. Fortunately, there have been only a small number of such crises in the past, and there is no present indication that we have to fear others, unless indeed we are made uncomfortable by the situation inside the nucleus of the atom.

Instrumentally and physically, energy is defined only through its differential, or, by extension, it is defined only with regard to a path leading from an initial to a final state. Formally, the energy difference between any pair of states will be independent of the path between them. The paper-and-pencil operation of integrating the differential of E along any joining path corresponds exactly to the physical operation of displacing the system along the path. But at this stage, a new purely paper-and-pencil element is injected into the situation. For it is a mathematical theorem that any function of two variables (that is, of the initial and the final state) which satisfies the conditions met here that it is independent of the path, may be analysed into the sum of two functions, one of the initial state only and the other of the final state only. Or formulated mathematically, the solution of the functional equation

$$f(x,y) + f(y,z) = f(x,z) \text{ is } f(x,y) = \phi(x) - \phi(y),$$

where $\phi(x)$ is arbitrary for any one particular x and the form of ϕ is determined in every special case by the form of f. That is, all the experimental values of the change of E for every state couple may be summarised by assigning to every *single* state its appropriate number and taking differences. This use of a single number associated with each single state obviously constitutes an enormous simplification for calculation and no physicist would for a moment entertain the thought of getting rid of the energy function at which we arrive in this way. It must not be forgotten, however, that this use of an energy function of the single state is something to which we have been led by the requirements of our paper-and-pencil operations, not of our instrumental operations, and that by so doing we have interjected something into the situation beyond the scope of our instruments. Almost never is there complete and unique correspondence between the instrumental and the paper-and-pencil domain—here the paper-and-pencil domain contains more than the instrumental domain. If we forget this, we are likely to read back into the instrumental situation implications carried over from the paper-and-pencil situation. This, I think, is what has happened when the energy concept is reified and energy assimilated conceptually to the concept of ' thing.' There can be no doubt, I think, that the energy concept is thus reified in the thinking of many scientists and certainly in the thinking of the man in the street. It is not uncommon to hear such statements as : ' the universe is composed of two things, matter and energy.' This point of view takes particular comfort and support from the Einstein mass-energy relation $E = m\,c^2$. But strictly, the above equation should be written $\Delta E = c^2 \Delta m$, and the deltas refer to an initial and a final state of a system. Even as applied to the atomic bomb, the mass energy relation by itself cannot tell us what to expect. What the equation does tell is that if a certain nuclear disintegration occurs and if a certain change of mass is found by experiment to accompany this disintegration that then we may expect a certain liberation of energy to accompany the reaction. ' Liberation of energy' itself implies an initial and a final state. One had no reason to expect that energy could be got out of the atom until it had been established by experiment that some nuclear reactions are accompanied by a loss of mass.

Energy is too complex to be assimilated to a thing and it should not be reified. 'Energy' is an aspect of the book-keeping by which we keep track of how far we have gone from our original configuration. The physics gets into the situation through the limitations imposed by nature on the sort of departures from the original configurations that are possible, and because of the character of these limitations our book-keeping most fortunately turns out to be gratifyingly simple.

We now consider another implication of the first law in the form $de = dQ + dW$. Since this law is ostensibly of a complete generality it applies not only to the original system but also to any sub-system which can be carved out of the original system in any way, not only by actual physical division, but in the paper-and-pencil domain by drawing imaginary surfaces in any way in the interior of the original system or even in the space outside it. For any conceivable sub-system the equation must have meaning, and this implies that it makes sense to speak of the energy in the form of heat or of work entering the system from outside. 'From outside' means across the boundaries, and at any particular point of space the boundary may be given any orientation whatever. It would therefore seem that the dQ and the dW must imply the existence of fluxes; in particular if heat enters a system from outside it must enter by flowing across the boundary, so that there is a flow vector for heat, $\vec{q}$, such that $dQ = $ -div $\vec{q}$, where now we write the dQ for unit time. Similarly, for mechanical energy, there must be a flow vector $\vec{w}$, such that $dW = $ -div $\vec{w}$. The implication is that these fluxes, to which we are thus led by the demands of our paper-and-pencil operations, have instrumental significance. For mechanical energy in its various forms these fluxes are already recognised. If the mechanical energy is ordinary stress-strain energy in an elastic solid, then $\vec{w}$ has a known value in terms of the stresses and the velocities of the elastic solid. If the energy is energy of the electromagnetic field, then its flow vector is given by the conventional Poynting vector. In all cases the flux of generalised mechanical energy at any point in space, either occupied or 'empty,' can thus be determined in terms of specifiable instrumental operations. Furthermore, the operations are made at the point in question. From this point of view the flux of mechanical energy may be said to have physical 'reality'—in fact this is the operational meaning of 'reality'

27

under these circumstances. Similarly, the flux vector for heat, $\vec{q}$, may be supposed to have operational instrumental meaning at every point although the situation is more complicated here than for mechanical energy. Inside material bodies by far the major part of heat is transported by conduction. There seems to be no simple instrument that responds to a flow of conduction heat, but such heat flow may be determined in terms of the temperature gradient at the point and the thermal conductivity of the material. In 'empty' space, transport of heat by radiation receives its instrumental meaning in terms of manipulations with perfectly absorbing screens. In ordinary substances, particularly if they are transparent, there must be a certain amount of heat transported by radiation as well as by conduction. I think it is not clear that in all cases it is possible to make a clean-cut separation of the heat thus transported into two parts, or to give a completely satisfactory instrumental specification for determining the total heat transport. In fact, there is a difficulty of principle here, which I think has not been completely resolved, for strictly, temperature is defined only in systems in equilibrium and in such systems heat is transported neither by conduction nor radiation. We shall not attempt to pursue the matter further here, but optimistically hope that the effect is not important in the situations of practice where temperature gradients or radiational fields are not too intense.

We shall accept the implication that the first law as conventionally formulated involves the existence of fluxes of heat and mechanical energy. We see that the existence of these fluxes has been implied by the demands of our paper-and-pencil operations, and that we have then been able to return from the paper-and-pencil domain to the instrumental domain and find there the physical fluxes which did not at first attract our attention. How this should be so we do not inquire—perhaps it is sufficient answer to say that the demands which we exact of our paper-and-pencil operations have themselves a tacit background of long instrumental experience. At any rate, it would appear that paper-and-pencil operations, or mental experiments in general, may have a useful role in suggesting programmes of investigation in the laboratory.

There is an interesting contrast between the relation of the paper-and-pencil. operations to the instrumental operations in the case of the fluxes as compared with the case of the energy. We have seen that the mathematics, in introducing a function of single states instead of

28

state pairs for the energy, has introduced a feature which has no counterpart in the physical situation. But with regard to the fluxes the situation is the inverse, because, although the fluxes have full instrumental significance, when it comes to subjecting them to paper-and-pencil operations we discard part of the full instrumental information, and use only the divergence of the fluxes. As far as the mathematics goes, we could add to all the fluxes any constant flux, no matter how large. Here again the mathematics does not exactly correspond to the instrumental situation, but now it is in defect rather than in excess. It is further to be remarked that although conventional thermodynamics utilises only the divergence aspect of the flux of energy in its two forms, a complete logical carrying through of all the verbal or paper-and-pencil implications of the flux aspect of energy eventually leads to the recognition of the tensor nature of energy, as it is treated in relativity theory. Such considerations would, however, take us much further than we can attempt to go here.

Consider now another implication of our paper-and-pencil demand with regard to dE, namely, that the first law have validity for every possible method of cutting the system into sub-systems. This implies that dE has meaning for every element of volume and this again means that the dE must be fully localised. It is not unusual to find the statement that the energy of thermodynamics is not localised, but that all we are concerned with is energy of the system as a whole. While this may be true in any specific case, I do not see how full localisation can be avoided if we are free to sub-divide our systems in any way. The dE thus localised may be found by the appropriate instrumental operations within each element of volume. These operations are not general, but have to be found by preliminary rehearsal. In the first instance, at the stage when the rules are being found by which the dE in any specific situation is to be determined, the first law is to be regarded as an equation of definition for dE. But once the rules have been found in terms of the state variables of the specific substance, the equation when applied in other situations loses its definitional character and acquires physical content. For now the equation states that the dE and the dQ and the dW, all determined by independent instrumental operations, will be found to be connected as the equation requires in all applications.

We have seen that the equation of the first law demands full localisation of energy, or more properly change of energy $\int dE$, and

29

that this localised energy may be determined by instrumental operations. This is all highly satisfactory, but there are other aspects of the situation which are curious and perhaps not in accord with our physical intuition. Consider the localisation of the energy in a system of electrostatic charges and in a system of gravitationally attracting masses. In the electrostatic system the energy is localised in the field in amount $\frac{1}{8\pi} E^2$ in each unit of volume. The energy so localised may be determined instrumentally at each element of volume merely by measuring the E with the proper instrument and making the calculation. Furthermore, when the configuration of the electrostatic system changes, the energy localised in an element of volume changes, which means that energy flows out of the element of volume. This flow of energy may be detected instrumentally by measuring the magnetic field in addition to the electrostatic field during the change and combining the electric and magnetic vectors in the well-known way to get the Poynting flux of energy. The situation is entirely different in the gravitational case, although mathematically the forces are given by inverse square laws in both cases. For in the gravitational case there is no detectable effect corresponding to the magnetic field, so that there is no flux of energy through empty space when the gravitational configuration changes. The result is that we cannot localise gravitational energy in the space surrounding the masses, but have to localise it in the masses themselves. This we can consistently do. If a gravitating system freely changes its configuration without constraint, then as the masses accelerate, there is a conversion of potential energy into kinetic energy within each mass, the total energy localised within each mass remaining constant. Or if the gravitating masses approach each other under constraints and so under approximately equilibrium conditions, then the necessary transport of gravitational energy from one mass to another takes place through the elastic members which serve as constraints, according to the mechanical Poynting vector in terms of the stresses and velocities. In no case do we have to have flux of gravitational energy through the surrounding 'empty' space, and this is consistent with the empirical finding that there is no instrumental indication of such a flux in space.

The situation is thus far satisfactory. But it is not so satisfactory when one considers that we would have been obliged to give the localisation of the gravitational case to the electrostatic case if it were not for the known magnetic field surrounding charges in motion, and that these magnetic fields are difficult to detect and were demonstrated only comparatively recently by highly skilled experimentation. Hence, at first, one hundred and fifty years ago, electrostatic energy would have had to be localised in the charges ; this is indeed possible mathematically as is demonstrated in any text on electrostatics. However, it does not feel right physically that so drastic a change of localisation of energy, from residing in the charges to being dispersed through infinite space, should be the result of the discovery of the mere existence of a force so small that for a long time it was below the possibility of detection. In fact, the gravitational situation appears to me so repulsive to physical intuition, which I suspect means merely my tacit verbal demands, that it seems to me we may well be on the lookout for a new gravitational effect, analogous to the magnetic field, too small to have yet been detected.

One may also feel uncomfortable in the face of other aspects of the energy situation. It does not feel right that energy should continually circulate indefinitely in closed paths in the complete static case of a superposed electrostatic and magnetostatic field. It is also to be remembered that although energy ' flows,' we can assign no identity to the flowing energy, so that we cannot say that the energy which was there is now here, and therefore we can assign no ' velocity ' to the flow as we can to the flow of a thing. This points up the remark we have already made. Although energy is in certain aspects like a thing, in its conservation and now in its localisation, it is certainly not like a thing in all respects, and is not to be reified.

Another feature in the energy situation which has unsatisfactory aspects, is that the flow vectors, $\vec{q}$ and $\vec{w}$, are not completely determined by the demands that we have put upon them. For all that we have demanded is that they be such as to give the correct dQ and dW, the latter being scalar quantities associated with the elements of volume. This amounts mathematically to the only demand put on the $\vec{q}$ and $\vec{w}$ being that their divergencies should have the proper values. But a vector is not uniquely determined by its divergence. On the other hand, our physical intuition demands that these flow vectors be capable of instrumental detection, and this means incidentally that they be unique. It is true that we have seen that such unique instrumental specification is possible, but to the extent that the uniqueness is not necessary we have not fully employed our instrumental information in constructing our thermodynamics.

The energy defined by the first law has, as we have discussed it thus far, great generality, but it is subject to at least one limitation as shown by the formulation, namely, we have defined it only in circumstances such that dQ and dW have meaning, or what is the equivalent, circumstances for which $\vec{q}$ and $\vec{w}$ have meaning. Now I think it is evident that the total energy flowing into a system cannot always be analysed into a thermal and a mechanical part. If one goes back to the original definitions of calorimetry he will see that the concept of heat and heat flow were formed under the express restriction that there was no motion of the parts of the system. That is, it is assumed that the heat which enters a system is measured in the absence of mechanical effects and similarly that the mechanical energy is measured in the absence of thermal effects. This last restriction is particularly applicable in radiational fields. How shall we separate the two effects when we have both mechanical and thermal effects, as in the convective cooling of a body in a rapidly stirred fluid with small scale turbulence? With what instrument shall we separate thermal from mechanical effects in a medium with small scale turbulence? Or, if there is frictional generation of heat on the surface of a system, the analysis into heat and work flow encounters infelicities.

How shall we handle situations in which we cannot assign a definite instrumental meaning to heat and work? Let us suppose in the first place that we are dealing with systems composed of substances for which the dE has been established by previous experiments for every specific substance as a specific function of the variables of state. This means that for any configuration of the system we are in a position to localise completely the energy as a scalar in every element of volume, and our only source of embarrassment arises because we do not know how to specify adequately the processes by which the localised energy changes. We at first deal with this situation formally and verbally. We lump together the $\vec{q}$ and the $\vec{w}$, unknown in detail, into a generalised flux of energy, which has to satisfy the requirement that its divergence is equal to the time rate of change of the localised energy. This latter requirement is merely the mathematical form of the statement : ' If energy is not created, then the increase of energy in unit time within any element of volume is equal to the amount of energy which has entered the volume across its boundaries in the same time.' This is, I think, in the first place a purely formal verbal demand which is imposed by the necessities of our thinking apparatus. If we assume that the increase of energy has independent instrumental meaning, as now it has, this formal statement contains two terms,

32

otherwise unknown, which are to that extent defined by the statement itself. These two terms are 'creation' and 'energy entering across the boundaries.' Since we are going to operate under the assumption that energy is conserved and therefore not created, we are left with a single undefined term, namely the flux of energy across the boundaries. Mathematically, a flux can always be found which shall have a specified divergence, so that our method of treatment involves no inconsistency. But the scheme acquires physical significance only when we can find some instrumental operation which independently measures flux of energy across the boundary. I think that a generalised instrumental operation for measuring flux of energy as such, without an analysis into thermal and mechanical components, has not been devised up to the present, and that therefore the device by which we save the flux of energy situation remains on the formal level, where it serves the function of giving consistency and completeness to our paper-and-pencil treatment. This does not mean at all that the other aspect of energy, that is, energy as a scalar localised in the volume elements of the system, is confined to the formal level ; for this aspect of the energy concept is susceptible of the most thoroughgoing instrumental verification. For if we suppose a universe of substances for which their scalar energy functions have been determined in terms of their variables of state, we may then select from this universe every conceivable combination in every conceivable initial condition, imprison any of these combinations in an adiabatic enclosure and check by instrumental measurement that the sum of the energy functions for every stage of all conceivable interactions is constant. In fact, the number of degrees of freedom attending all possible reactions in an adiabatic enclosure is so great that we may invert the process, and by studying the adiabatic reactions of a new unknown substance with other known substances, find how to assign an energy function to the new substance. In this way we could deal with a substance which takes part in no processes for which the flow of heat and mechanical work are separately defined. But always in the back-ground, in order to get started, we have to assume some substance whose energy function has been established by processes for which heat and work have meaning. In practice this imposes no restriction at all.

In practice, when dealing with unfamiliar forms of energy flow, we may invert the sequence suggested by the definition, and having found the scalar energy function for some substance, use that to determine the energy flow. This is essentially what is done when the flow of radiant energy is measured in terms of the rise of temperature of a screen placed in its path. It does not appear, however, why the energy flow determined in this way should be described, as it usually is, as a flow of radiant *heat*. There are situations in which this method of description may lead to infelicities, particularly when the flow is unidirectional. It would seem preferable to describe this flow as, at least partly, a flow of mechanical energy rather than as heat.

It is interesting to observe how the significance of the equation of the first law, $dE = dQ + dW$, for those systems to which it is applicable, has changed as use of the equation has extended. It began as a formal equation of definition of dE, and therefore with a strong paper-and-pencil component of significance. It has ended as an equation in which each term has independent instrumental significance, and therefore as an equation which in any specific situation is capable of complete instrumental verification. As such, it has evolved from a definition to a statement of a 'natural law.' We may, if we like, take this as the definition of 'natural law.'

The question of separating energy in the form of heat from that in the form of work is not of great importance when we are dealing with the first law alone, but it is vital when we deal with the second law. A completely satisfactory method of separating the two concepts of work and heat, even in principle, has not I believe yet been found. At least one serious attempt to place thermodynamics on a logically rigorous foundation by the use of the postulational method, with which I have been familiar, failed because a distinction in principle between heat and work could not be formulated with sufficient precision.

We now turn to a consideration of certain aspects of the second law. We start with the conventional mathematical formulation of the law in the form : $dS = dQ/t$. Here dS is the change of entropy of the system in question for any reversible process during which the heat dQ is absorbed. The equation as it stands is at first a definition for dS. But just as in the case of the first law, the equation is supplemented by the statement that the dS so defined is a perfect differential in the state variables of the system. It follows that the total increment of entropy, obtained by integrating dS, on passing from any fixed initial state to any fixed final state is independent of the details of the process and depends only on the initial and final states. Again, as in the case of the energy, it is convenient mathematically to deal with this situation by choosing some arbitrary state as the initial state and assign an arbitrary value of entropy to it. By application of the second law the other states of the system may then be assigned single entropy numbers and the difference of entropy between any two states may then be found by taking the difference of the corresponding entropy numbers. With this understanding it is convenient to speak of the entropy as a state function, but as with the case of energy, this must not obscure the essential fact that we are strictly concerned with a state couple and that it is only differences of entropy that have physical significance or are uniquely defined.

The entropy may be determined as a function of state for any specific substance for such states as can be reached by reversible operations. The entropy having been thus determined, the equation of the second law changes its character, becoming no longer merely an equation of definition, but it acquires complete physical status and states an equality which will be found experimentally to hold between two independently instrumentally determined things, namely the difference of entropy between any two states and the integral taken over any reversible path connecting them. The necessity for finding at least one reversible method of reaching the final from the initial state does not in ordinary practice lead to any onerous restriction, for such a reversible process can usually be discovered. There are cases, however, where the restriction is onerous, and there are even cases where it seems impossible in principle to remove the restriction. We will return to this question.

Just as in the case of energy, the entropy to which we are thus led must be accorded full localisation in space, because the system can be divided into subsystems in any arbitrary way and the second law applied to every arbitrary element. This demands the existence of fluxes of entropy to account for the changes of localised entropy, just as we had to have fluxes of energy. The necessity for the existence of a flux of entropy is at first a consequence of a purely formal and verbal demand. The formulation of this demand is a little different in the case of entropy than for energy because we do not have conservation of entropy. The demand in the case of entropy is thus more general than it was for energy and may be formulated as follows : ' The excess of entropy in any given region of space at the end of any interval of time over that which was present at the beginning of the interval, is equal to the entropy which has entered the region across the boundaries in the same interval, plus that which was created within

35

the region during the same interval.' As it stands this is completely formal and verbal and devoid of any factual content, but I think it represents a form of thought without which we could not conveniently operate. It is formal because we have not as yet any instrumental method of giving meaning to flow of entropy across the boundaries or to 'creation of entropy.' We now seek to give factual content to our formal and conventional demand by discovering instrumental operations corresponding to flow and creation. Whatever instrumental operations we discover must be subject to the restriction that their relation to each other is consistent with our formal demand.

It is only comparatively recently that the recognition has been growing that the full thermodynamic picture presented by both our instrumental and paper-and-pencil operations demands the existence of a flow vector for entropy and also a 'creation function.' Not only this, but it is coming to be realised that flow and creation provide the tools by which certain irreversible processes may be brought within the ambit of thermodynamics. It is notorious that classical thermodynamics has only a very limited applicability to irreversible processes. Beyond stating that the total entropy of the universe increases during any irreversible process it can do very little ; it does not attempt to state how great the increase of entropy is or where it is situated. Physics should not be thus impotent, and it does not accept such impotence in other fields. We may recognise two kinds of irreversibility. The first arises from too great complexity of the process, as when a gas expands turbulently through an opening from a region at one pressure to a region at a lower pressure. Here our failure to deal with the situation arises from our inability to describe exhaustively what is going on in terms of measurements with the large scale instruments which measure the variables of state.

In addition to these complicated processes, there are simple irreversible processes which can be completely specified in terms of a few simple measurements and it would seem that we ought to be able to deal with these. Perhaps the simplest of all such irreversible processes is the steady flow of heat by conduction down a temperature gradient. Let us analyse this simple situation and see whether we can find a plausible way of assigning a flow of entropy and a creation of entropy. We may imagine the heat conduction taking place through a conducting bridge connecting two heat reservoirs at different temperatures. The reservoirs themselves are idealised as usual by supposing them made of material which is an infinitely good conductor of heat. This ensures that the heat imparted to the reservoir from outside is uniformly distributed through it by a reversible process. In the final steady state, the hot reservoir is continually losing entropy because it is losing heat, and the cold reservoir is continually gaining entropy. The conducting bridge remains in a steady state, and because of our principle that its entropy is a function of the state variables, its entropy is not changing. If the quantity of heat Q passes by conduction from the hot reservoir at temperature t_2 to the colder reservoir at temperature t_1, the loss of entropy of the hot reservoir is Q/t_2 and the gain of entropy of the cold reservoir Q/t_1, and since the conducting bridge does not change, the gain of entropy of the universe is $Q(1/t_1 - 1/t_2)$. We must say that the entropy of the cold reservoir increases because entropy flows into it, and the entropy of the hot reservoir decreases because entropy flows out of it. By the principle of sufficient reason we must say that entropy flows into the reservoir where the conducting bridge joins it. If $\vec{q}$ is the flow vector corresponding to Q, that is, the vector given by Q divided by the time of flow, then these demands force us to say that the entropy flow vector where the conducting bridge connects with the colder reservoir is $\vec{q}/t_1$, and similarly the flow vector where the bridge connects with the hot reservoir is $\vec{q}/t_2$. We would be going out of our way not to suppose that in general, whenever we have heat flow by conduction, the corresponding entropy flow is $\vec{q}/t$. Apply this vector now to the conducting bridge and consider an element of volume bounded by two surfaces perpendicular to the axis of the bridge. The vector $\vec{q}$ is constant all down the bridge. Since the exit temperature of our element of volume is lower than the entrance temperature, our expression for vector flow demands that the entropy flowing out be greater than the entropy flowing in. But since, as we have already seen, no entropy is accumulating within the region because the state is steady, this can only mean according to our formal demand that entropy is being created within the region. On reflection this appears as it should be. For the volume element is the seat of a continuous steady irreversible process leading to the continual entropy increase of the universe and what more natural than that the entropy should be created in the region where the irreversible process occurs? But the entropy having been created, does not remain in its place of origin, but is immediately transported away to find its final resting place elsewhere, in the reservoirs.

It is easy to find a general mathematical expression for the entropy created which reduces to the correct value in the simple case just described. This is :

$$\left(\begin{matrix} \text{Entropy created per unit} \\ \text{time per unit volume} \end{matrix}\right) = - \frac{\vec{q} \cdot \text{Grad } \tau}{\tau^2}.$$

It is natural to postulate that whenever we have conduction of heat, which is always an irreversible process, we have a creation of entropy according to the equation just given, whether or not the conduction process is accompanied by other reversible or irreversible processes. This postulate gives to ' creation of entropy,' in the case of heat conduction, the independent instrumental significance that we have been seeking. If other irreversible processes occur jointly with heat conduction, and if we can similarly find the ' creation ' to be associated with them, then we have given full instrumental status to ' creation.' In addition to the creation function, we have also, in the case of thermal conduction, found the flow vector. Let us suppose that we have similarly found an appropriate flow vector for other processes. Then we have given full instrumental status to our statement which in the first instance was formal and conventional, namely : ' Entropy accumulating within a region of space is equal to that created within the region augmented by the amount which has flowed in across the boundaries.' We have now a statement which is capable of complete instrumental verification. Let us assume that the experimental verification is complete. How shall we describe our result ? I think we would not say that we have thereby verified the statement, but rather that we have verified the correctness of our expressions for creation and flow of entropy. The form of the statement is, I think, one to which we would cling no matter what the experimental situation. The form thus has only a verbal and not a physical significance, but there is, nevertheless, a certain compulsion associated with it.

Going back, there are other simple physical processes beside thermal conductivity for which it is possible to find appropriate creation and flow functions for entropy. A particularly simple case is the generation of heat by an electrical current flowing against a resistance. This is an essentially irreversible process, for which it proves that the appropriate expression for the creation of entropy per unit time per unit volume is simply ri^2/τ, where r is the specific resistance of the material. The heat generated by the current flows away from the place of generation by conduction and thus provides an entropy flow vector,

$\bar{q}/\tau$ by which the entropy ri^2/τ is carried away. This entropy flow is adequate to carry away the generated entropy, and thus may be taken as the entropy flow vector, and thus may be taken as the entropy flow vector for irreversible entropy generation by a current in overcoming electrical resistance, except for a small term, which can usually be neglected, to which we shall return in the third lecture.

The creation function for entropy being known for thermal conduction and electrical resistance, we are in a position to check the correctness of our views by application to a special problem. This is the problem of the thermoelectric circuit. There are certain relations between various thermal effects and the electromotive force in such a circuit which are known empirically and are so simple that we should be able to deduce them. Since the entire source of the electrical energy is thermal, we should be able to deduce the relations by a thermodynamic argument. The relations were thus deduced by Lord Kelvin, but only by an argument which he himself recognised to be lacking in rigour. What Kelvin did was to entirely disregard the irreversible processes in a thermoelectric circuit, and deduce the relation by supposing that only reversible processes occurred. Now this is usually legitimate in the elementary situations of thermodynamics. For usually it is possible to give the system such dimensions or otherwise modify it so that the irreversible aspects may be made vanishingly small in comparison with the reversible ones. This is ordinarily done, for example, by conducting the processes infinitely slowly, or by using infinitely good conducting material for the reservoirs, or some similar device. Now it turns out that the thermoelectric circuit occupies a quite unusual position with regard to the possibility of making the irreversible processes of vanishing importance. For there are two irreversible processes in the thermoelectric circuit, thermal conduction, and development of heat by Joulean heating, which are so connected by the physics of the situation that they cannot both be made vanishingly small simultaneously, but when one is made small by suitable choice of dimensions or otherwise, the other becomes large. It follows that both cannot be made to vanish, so that the total amount of dissipation in the system compared with the useful utilisation always has a finite value. An upper limit can be set rigorously to the ratio of these two effects by the fundamental inequality of classical thermodynamics. But when the numerical values are substituted which correspond to this inequality, one side of the inequality turns out to be one thousand times larger than the other, so that no useful information at all is given by the rigorous expression. This was first shown by Boltzmann.

No such difficulty arises, however, if this problem is treated according to the point of view that each of the two irreversible processes is accompanied by its own characteristic creation of entropy, unmodified by the occurrence of the other processes. For now we can write down the entropy generation of the entire process, including both reversible and irreversible parts, and from this eliminate the contribution arising from the irreversible parts, because now we know its exact quantitative value, and remain with a relation between the reversible parts. This turns out to be exactly the relation derived by Kelvin by unsatisfactory argument, and furthermore is checked by experiment with a precision which becomes continually better with each improvement in the measurements. The same sort of argument can be extended to similar situations, and in my book on *The Thermodynamics of Electrical Phenomena in Metals* will be found several applications, particularly to the deduction of transverse thermoelectric effects in crystals.

The same method of handling irreversibility has essentially been employed by Eckart for two other processes so simple that they can be completely characterised in terms of a few measurements with macroscopic instruments, namely the processes of viscous flow in a fluid and of diffusion down a concentration gradient. In his analysis Eckart[1] has found how to write explicit expressions for the entropy created when the process runs. The expressions are simple and appear intuitively natural. They localise the creation of entropy where it would be expected, that is, where the irreversible process occurs. The permanent abiding place of the increase of entropy is, however, elsewhere, the entropy being conducted away on the flow vector, from its place of origin as soon as created. Eckart also found the appropriate expressions for the flow.

In a recent paper Tolman and Fine[2] summarised these applications and have emphasised the creation and flow aspects of entropy. In Belgium, De Donder[3] and his school, notably Prigogine[4] have been much occupied with such questions, particularly with irreversible

[1] C. Eckart, Phys. Rev. 58, 267, 269, 1940
[2] R. C. Tolman and P. C. Fine, Rev. Mod. Phys. 20, 51, 1948
[3] Th. De Donder and P. Van Rysselberghe, *Thermodynamic Theory of Affinity, A Book of Principles*, Stanford University Press, 1936
[4] I. Prigogine, Etude Thermodynamique des Phénomènes Irréversibles, Thesis, Liege, 1947

chemical reactions. But as far as I know all such analysis up to the present has been confined to cases where there is some method of assigning an entropy to the material within which the irreversible process occurs, that is, where some reversible method exists for getting from the initial to the final state. If the entropy can thus be independently evaluated, it is a comparatively straightforward problem to work out the creation and flow functions. But I believe that the general problem of irreversibility is not as simple as this and that the fundamental difficulty in the general case is in knowing whether an entropy exists, and, if so, in finding how to evaluate it. For, going back to the original definition, entropy is defined as a state function only for those states for which at least one reversible method exists for getting from the standard state of reference to the state in question. But many of the bodies of experience are in such a state that every change to which the body is subjected contains some component of irreversibility. An example is any piece of metal which has been heavily strained plastically. That is, many of the materials of daily life, perhaps most of them, are completely isolated by irreversibility from the universe of thermodynamics, so that in principle the classical concept of entropy is not applicable to them. Incidentally, the whole living world of biology is thus isolated. Strictly it cannot be asked whether living things violate the second law of thermodynamics, because the entropy concept, in terms of which the second law is formulated, does not apply. For if the entropy concept were applicable, it would involve some reversible method of getting from the non-living to the living, and this involves at the least the artificial creation of life, an operation which we cannot at present perform.

Returning to the plastically strained metal, strictly we cannot speak of its entropy, and if we find how to do so, it must be by an extension of the classical entropy concept. Now it would be most desirable if we could so extend the entropy concept. One reason is that statistical mechanics represents entropy as one of the most universal of the properties of matter and sets up specific methods for calculating it with no reference to reversibility or irreversibility. It would be desirable if some connection could be found between the statistical concept and the thermodynamic entropy concept in this more general setting.

What requirements shall we place on an extended thermodynamic entropy ? It must, of course, reduce to the known values in the limiting case of reversibility. In addition, during the irreversible

41

process it would seem that we must also demand that the total entropy of the universe always increase at every stage of the irreversible process and that the region of entropy creation be the region where the irreversibility is taking place. These demands are perhaps not sufficient to give us a unique solution, so that in a first exploration of the possibilities we will naturally choose a solution which appears most simply to satisfy the conditions. I have examined the possibility of such an extension to several comparatively simple non-steady irreversible processes, namely the cyclic deformation of a body with stress-strain hysteresis, the deformation of the conventional idealised perfectly plastic body satisfying the von Mises criterion, and a body in which an internal irreversible generation of heat may take place as in the unmixing of a mixed crystal.[1] In all these cases it is possible to find a simple expression for the rate of entropy creation and also for the entropy to be associated with the body in which the irreversible process occurs. Whether the precise expressions found by the simple analysis are the correct ones, will have to be found by experiment. At present the experimental basis has not been sufficiently laid for a thoroughgoing critique, and we have to be satisfied with the crude indication that there seems to be no glaring inconsistency.

It would appear, therefore, that there is nothing intrinsically contradictory in attempting to generalise and extend the entropy concept beyond the range of its classical definition and into the range of intrinsically irreversible processes. For each special kind of irreversible process the details will have to be worked out. Entropy has no more a universal instrumental significance than does energy. This detailed working out will involve a background of complete experimental knowledge, which means the ability to exhaustively describe the phenomena with macroscopic measurements. Once having acquired such command, it would appear that we may attack the problem by methods in the spirit, if not the letter, of classical thermodynamics. A final failure of the thermodynamic approach may be anticipated only in those cases where we can not acquire sufficient command of the situation to be able to exhaustively describe it.

[1] P. W. Bridgman, Rev. Mod. Phys. 22, 56, 1950

III

In this third lecture we shall examine some of the concepts by which we describe various elementary electrical phenomena in massive conductors carrying electrical currents. As in the second lecture, we shall be largely concerned with separating the instrumental from the paper-and-pencil operations, in seeing how we construct our paper-and-pencil operations so as to satisfy certain basic verbal demands, and in examining what sort of correspondence is attainable between the verbal demands and the instrumental operations.

It is, I think, the general opinion that the classical scheme of description of electrical phenomena in conductors, as contained for example in Maxwell's equations, is adequate for a description of all the macroscopic aspects of current flow. I believe, however, that this is not the case, but that when we push the implications of our paper-and-pencil operations to the limit, and demand that we be able to describe the result of any conceivable mental experiment, we shall find that we have to supplement the classical scheme in certain respects and modify it by recognising distinctions which can be ignored in the simpler situations. In order not unnecessarily to complicate the issues we shall, in most of the following, concern ourselves only with steady current flow in systems with no moving parts and of such small dimensions that the velocity of light propagation may be neglected. This means that the electric vector at every point can be calculated from the distribution of macroscopic static charges by the inverse square law and is therefore derivable from a potential function. The magnetic field can be calculated from the currents. We shall, however, allow the electrical system to be composed of different metals with temperature differences between the parts (which may be maintained at steady values by appropriate thermal reservoirs) so that the system is the seat of thermo-electromotive forces and of the conversion of thermal into electrical energy. We shall find, I think, that the conventional macroscopic scheme of description is not adequate to represent all the interactions between electrical and thermal energy, but it will have to be supplemented.

Our equations, that is, our paper-and-pencil operations, employ a current vector which defines a density of current flow at every point of the interior of a massive conductor. This current density is, in the first instance, a constructed quantity as is any other thing pertaining to the inaccessible interior of a solid. However, its instrumental implications are so varied and numerous, that we can pretty well give current density full instrumental status. For the total integrated current may be given independent status by several different methods, as by measuring the quantity of electricity deposited when the conductor is connected to a condenser of large capacity, or by measuring the chemical decomposition in a Faraday experiment in electrolysis, or by computing the magnetic field in surrounding space (and checking with experiment). Furthermore, the assumed detailed distribution within the conductor may be checked by dividing the conductor into filaments along the lines of current flow, replacing each filament by a physically independent conductor, and then checking the flow in each filament by one of the means just suggested.

The presence of a current at any point of a conductor involves, according to the conventional picture, a force acting on the current at that point to maintain it against the electrical resistance. This force has full paper-and-pencil significance through the equation

$$\text{current density} = \frac{\text{intensity of force divided}}{\text{by specific resistance}} \quad . \quad . \quad (1)$$

The specific resistance, of course, has full instrumental significance through independent measurement. The situation with respect to the instrumental significance of the force is somewhat more complex. In certain simple situations, as in the interior of a homogeneous massive conductor all at the same temperature, we could give a somewhat impractical instrumental significance in terms of the force that would be experienced by a microscopic test charge in a cavity excavated in the conductor, proper correction being made for the charges which would appear by induction on the walls of the cavity. Also, in this simple case we can give independent paper-and-pencil significance to the force in terms of calculations by the inverse square law from the total distribution of electric charge. But in the general case, in particular when there are chemical inhomogeneities or temperature gradients, the force cannot be calculated in this way, and we

44

have to recognise the presence of a component in the force which is not given by the static charges. We may call this the 'non-field' force, since it cannot be deduced by the field equations from the charge distribution. In general, we have to recognise the existence of a 'non-field' force acting not only on currents but also on static electric charges. In particular, such a force, implied in the equations but almost never written out explicitly, is made necessary by the 'boiler pressure' tending to blow the static charge off the surface of a curved conductor. The charge is held in place by a counter force, not deducible from the equations. This counter force is sometimes described as a 'non-electric' force, but since in a sense any force acting on electricity is an 'electric' force, it would seem that the term 'non-field' force is perhaps a better description. Another example is afforded by any battery delivering a steady current. Within the battery current flows contrary to the direction of the field force derived from the static charges by the inverse square. There must be therefore within the battery a 'non-field' force, and furthermore this 'non-field' force is greater than the 'field' force. It is obviously connected with the 'electro-motive-force' of the battery, which in turn is connected with the energy delivered by the battery, so that the 'non-field' force has two aspects. In the case of the simple battery, there is a simple relation between the two aspects of the 'non-field' force, that is, the aspect relating to current flow against resistance and the aspect relating to energy. In the general case, however, the same simple relation does not hold between these two aspects as holds for a battery.

In addition to the two examples just given, there is in simple isothermal systems another 'non-field' force. This is located in the surface of the metal, as is also the force equilibrating the 'boiler pressure' of the surface charge, but it is not related to the boiler pressure and is connected with the Volta effect. It is well known that the surfaces of two different metals in contact with each other and all at the same temperature will come to a difference of electrical potential, characteristic of the two metals. Because of this difference of potential the space surrounding the metals becomes the seat of an electric force, which has full instrumental status since it may be measured with an exploring charge. Since the entire surface of either single metal is at the same potential, the metal being a conductor, it follows that the Volta potential difference demands a discontinuous jump in the potential where the two metals join. Mathematically a jump in potential

45

demands infinite electrical charges spaced an infinitesimal distance apart. The facts of the Volta phenomenon can be explained by supposing the surfaces of the two metals to be the seat of a potential jump, and therefore of a double layer. This potential jump and consequent double layer may be situated on any of three possible surfaces, namely the two surfaces separating the metals from surrounding space and the surface on which the two metals are in contact. There is only one condition on these three double layers and the corresponding potential jumps, namely that together they give the observed instrumental Volta difference between the two metals. Evidently the one condition imposed by the Volta difference is not sufficient to determine the values in detail of the three jumps (but jump there must be somewhere).

The double layer on the surface of a conductor thus demanded by the Volta phenomenon does not have full instrumental significance. For a uniform double layer may be added to the surface of any isolated conductor without changing any instrumental result. For such a double layer has no effect at outside points, and within has the effect only of uniformly raising the potential everywhere by the same amount. Since this uniform increase of potential is accompanied by no change of electrical force, and since it is only electrical forces and not potentials that electrical instruments respond to, there is no way of giving instrumental meaning to the supposed double layer. This is a situation that makes our physical intuition profoundly uncomfortable (for the picture that we form of the double layer on the surface is drawn with the same physical elements, positive and negative charges, as have instrumental significance in other situations), and it does not seem right that we should not be able to determine uniquely what double charge is on any given surface. In the absence of any instrumental method of giving the answer we may try to find the answer in the paper-and-pencil domain by connecting with some theory. It proves, however, that as long as we stay in the domain of macroscopic phenomena governed by the classical field equations, no theory gives a unique answer to this question. Historically there have been two important different points of view. Lord Kelvin believed that the entire Volta jump originated in the surface of separation of the two metals in contact, whereas Maxwell and Heaviside would have no potential jump at this surface (except for the small Peltier jump to be discussed later), and put the jumps at the surfaces separating the metals from surrounding space. Both protagonists attempted to prove their position by one sort of argument or another, but I believe that there are no macroscopic phenomena covered by the equations which permit a decision between these two. In particular, the contention of Heaviside that a decision could be reached on the basis of the transformations of energy I believe to be unsound, since the Poynting vector, in the regions where it is incapable of instrumental verification, that is, within the hypothetical double layers, is capable of so adjusting itself as adequately to account for any particular energy manifestation that may be demanded by any particular hypothesis about the double layers. More than this, in our present wider experimental range, in which are included such new operations as taking electricity through a surface into the surrounding space, as in the phenomena of electron emission, I believe that we are still unable to give full instrumental status to the existence of these potential jumps and double layers, and their meaning is still to be sought partially in the paper-and-pencil domain. This may appear unsatisfactory, but it is not unlike other situations. The instrumentally meaningless isolated double layer may remind one of the instrumentally meaningless single valued energy that our mathematics would find congenial. Both of these concepts find their instrumental meaning only in complex situations with a plurality of elements.

Let us now consider systems in which we have different metals and temperature differences, but no chemical action. We may typify this by the conventional thermoelectric circuit shown in Figure 1, in which we have two homogeneous metals A and B leading from a

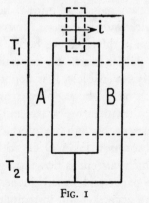

FIG. 1

region all at one temperature, T_1, to a region all at another, T_2, within the regions the metals being in contact. Such an arrangement is the seat of an electric current which may be used to deliver energy through

47

a motor, and therefore is also the seat of an electromotive force. The energy delivered by the current has full instrumental status as does also the current, so that the E.M.F. also has full instrumental status through the definition,

Energy delivered by current in unit time equals

current × E.M.F. . . . . . . (2)

The 'energy delivered' here means mechanical work done by the motor plus the heating effect of the current in overcoming Joulean resistance. The latter has instrumental status, either directly, or through the equation ; Joulean heating in unit time equals i^2R, R being measureable and with full instrumental status. By definition, the thermoelectric power of the circuit is the E.M.F. for unit temperature difference between the junctions. The thermoelectric power may be written as dE_{AB}/dT where E_{AB} is the total E.M.F. of a couple composed of the metals A and B, reaching from an arbitrary constant lower temperature to a variable upper temperature T. The order of the subscripts indicates that on closed circuit current flows from A to B at the hot junction. In general, dE_{AB}/dT is a function of the average temperature of the couple. The source of energy is thermal, there being no other possibility, such as chemical transformations. As a consequence certain thermal phenomena occur in the system when current is flowing which do not otherwise take place. There are two sorts of these phenomena. One takes place at the interface between the two metals in contact, and the other in the body of the homogeneous metal where there is a temperature gradient. At the interface between the two metals additional heat has to be supplied from some outside source when current flows to maintain the same temperature distribution in the circuit as before the current was made. This heat is called the Peltier heat. By experiment it is proportional to the current and fully reversible. It is denoted by P_{AB}, and is defined as the heat which has to be supplied from outside to maintain the original *status quo* of temperature when unit quantity of electricity is transported by the current through the interface in the direction from A to B. This heat absorption takes place within the solid metal at the interface across which current is flowing. Strictly it should perhaps be regarded as a paper-and-pencil quantity, but it would be a super-refinement not to accord it full instrumental status, because the total heat fed into the general neighbourhood of the junction from outside has full instrumental status, and the same value is found experimentally in a wide variety of dimensions and proportions for the circuits.

The second thermal effect takes place in the body of the metal when current flows through a temperature gradient. By definition it is the extra heat, in addition to the Joulean heat, supplied by the surroundings to maintain the original temperature *status quo* when unit quantity of electricity is transported by the current from one point to another one degree higher. This heat is called the Thomson heat, and for the metal A is denoted by σ_A, the subscript indicating that it is a function of the metal. It is also a function of the temperature. Within experimental error the Thomson heat, like the Peltier heat, is proportional to the current and reversible with it, and it has full instrumental status in the same sense as the Peltier heat.

There are relations between the two heats and the thermoelectric power of the couple. This topic has already been touched in the second lecture where it was mentioned that Kelvin first deduced these relations by an argument which he recognised as defective, by neglecting the irreversible aspects of the phenomena, which cannot be made to vanish (as they usually can in other similar situations) by any choice of the dimensions or manipulations of the rate of the process. It appeared that the same results could also be obtained, not by neglecting the irreversible phenomena, but by allowing them to occur in full swing and correcting for them by postulating that each of the two irreversible processes is accompanied by a characteristic increase of entropy. The formulas so obtained are,

$$P_{AB} = \tau \frac{dE_{AB}}{d\tau} . \qquad . \qquad . \qquad . \qquad . \quad (3)$$

$$\sigma_B - \sigma_A = \tau \frac{d^2 E_{AB}}{d\tau^2} . \qquad . \qquad . \qquad . \quad (4)$$

Every term in these formulas has full instrumental status, and the formulas have been abundantly checked by experiment. So long, therefore, as we are concerned only with the complete circuit we remain in the domain of completely instrumental quantities. But we leave this domain when we start talking about the action in parts of the circuit, as we are almost forced to when we start forming a theory of the action. For instance, in our theory we shall certainly want to apply the first law of thermodynamics, and this law, as we have seen, is applicable to any element of volume that can be cut out of the system. In particular we shall want to be able to say that the first law applies to the dotted element of volume in Figure 1. This means

49

that in the steady state (which we are assuming) the net energy flowing out of the region is zero, since energy is not created, and to formulate this we find ourselves at once in the midst of constructional paper-and-pencil quantities. The construction that we adopt will depend to a certain extent on our theory.

Let us begin by examining the account that Heaviside gave of this situation. He said that since there is in the complete circuit an E.M.F. which is equal to the total heat absorbed by the whole couple, and since heat is absorbed at the interface, it is obvious that there is an E.M.F. in the interface equal to the heat absorbed there, that is, equal to the Peltier heat. But now this E.M.F. at the interface implies a ' non-field ' force which will tend to produce a current. Furthermore, since the E.M.F. is finite and the region in which it acts is of infinitesimal thickness, the corresponding ' non-field ' force must be infinite, and this by itself would produce an infinite current, the specific resistance within the metal being everywhere finite. The infinite ' non-field ' force must therefore be counterbalanced at the interface by an equal and opposite field force, and this means a double layer of static charge of strength equal to the surface E.M.F., that is, equal to the Peltier heat. This double layer means a difference of potential on opposite sides of the surface of separation of the metals equal to the Peltier heat. This means an equal jump in potential in the space immediately outside the free surfaces of the metals across the line of separation. In addition to this exterior jump accompanying the interior jump there may also be a jump due to the Volta jumps, which Heaviside located on the external surfaces of A and B. These Volta jumps play no part in the present picture, however, since the Volta effect is by itself not a source of energy. We neglect the Volta jumps for the present analysis therefore. How now can Heaviside meet the energy demands on the element of volume embracing the surface AB ? Heat energy is flowing in of amount iP_{AB}. What is the compensating outflowing energy ? It appears at once that there is such a flow of energy in the Poynting vector. Because in the narrow external girdle surrounding the surface AB there is an intense electric field because of the potential jump. There is also a magnetic field because a current is flowing. The magnetic field is circumferential and the electric field along the axis of the wire, that is, at right angles to the magnetic field. There is therefore a Poynting vector perpendicular to the external surface of the conductor, and on working out the mathematical values it is found that the total energy carried away on the Poynting vector from the neighbourhood of the junction is exactly equal to the heat input, or, per unit time, equal to iP_{AB} or $i \triangle V$, where $\triangle V$ is the potential jump across the interface. Everything therefore comes out as it should, and Heaviside felt justified in his point of view. But even so, the solution does not have full instrumental status, as indeed it cannot when it is reflected that the solution is not unique. For the double layer can be modified by any arbitrary addition, provided only that a compensating addition is made at the other junction. For although there is an additional energy flow under such conditions, it is a closed flow, out of one junction and into the other, and cannot be distinguished instrumentally from a flow into the Volta double layer on the external surface of the wires.

In additional comment on the solution of Heaviside it is to be kept in mind for the later argument that he postulated in the interface AB a local E.M.F. which was the same fraction of the total E.M.F. of the circuit as the local heat is of the total heat.

It is obvious that the state of affairs at the surface AB must be dealt with by some sort of construction. It would also be desirable if this construction should be unique, because then we might hope to be able eventually to give it full instrumental status. I think it is obvious, however, that as long as we have only the considerations of Heaviside we will never be able to find a unique solution, but there will always be freedom with respect to how the potential jumps are distributed among the three possible surfaces. Fortunately, it turns out that there is an entirely new sort of experimental consideration which enables us to find a unique solution in certain simple cases, and in the general case a solution unique except for an arbitrary constant.

The new order of experimental fact is afforded by the behaviour of single metal crystals. It is an experimental fact that two rods cut in different orientations from the same non-cubic metal crystal will function like two different metals in a thermocouple. That is, a thermocouple may be constructed from the parallel and perpendicular orientations of a single crystal as indicated in Figure 2. In such a couple Peltier heat is absorbed at the interface when current flows across the interface from one orientation to the other, and where there are temperature gradients there are Thomson heats, $\sigma_{\parallel}$ or $\sigma_{\perp}$ depending on whether the current flow is parallel or perpendicular to the crystal axis. These heats, as in the case of the ordinary couple, are point functions, characteristic only of the metal (and the direction of current flow), and not dependent at any point on what may be happening at other points

51

of the circuit. Heaviside's point of view applied to this situation would demand that there is a jump of potential on going across a surface at which the orientation changes, and therefore a double layer

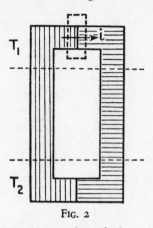

FIG. 2

at the interface characteristic only of the orientations. But this leads, for the crystal, to an impossible state of affairs. For consider the system at constant temperature represented by Figure 3, in which a

FIG. 3

piece has been cut out of a single crystal and reinserted in another orientation. Because it is at constant temperature, no currents can flow. Consider now the changes of potential encountered in describing the closed path $ABCDA$. By hypothesis in passing from A to B a jump of potential is encountered equal to $P_{\perp\parallel}$. From B to C no change of potential is encountered because this path is entirely within the single homogeneous metal in which the potential is constant, or otherwise current would flow. From C to D again exactly the same jump of potential is encountered as from A to B because the orientations are the same. Again from D to A there can be no change of potential. We have therefore returned to the starting point and the initial potential after encountering a total potential change of $2P_{\perp\parallel}$.

Therefore $P_{\perp\parallel}$ must be zero and there can be no potential jump and no double layer on crossing a surface at which the orientation changes.

With this new knowledge, let us return to an examination of the first law as applied to the dotted region in Figure 2. As before, the Peltier heat $P_{\perp\parallel}$ flows into the region. But now there is no potential jump and no electric field in the girdle surrounding the wire and hence no Poynting vector to carry off the energy to compensate for the inflowing heat. What other possible source of energy flow is there in this situation? It is evident, by the principle of sufficient reason, that only the current can play a part here. We are apparently almost forced to 'say' that the current carries out of the region energy equal to the inflowing heat energy. Let us see where we get by postulating an energy convected by the current. In order to be satisfactory I think we would demand that this postulated convected energy have certain properties. It must be a 'point function,' that is, the energy carried by the current at a point in the conductor must be determinable in principle (i.e. by mental experiments) in terms of instrumental operations made at the point in question. In other words the convected energy at a point must not depend on what is going on in other parts of the system. If this were the case the detailed expression for the convected energy at a point would change with every change in the gross geometry of the system at distant points, and would indeed be a mere convention. These requirements in the present case mean that the energy convected per unit current may be a function of the current itself, of the material in which it is flowing, of the direction of flow with respect to the crystal axis, of the temperature, and of nothing else, because these are all there are at the point. Apply now the first law to the element of volume of Figure 2. Denote by U the energy convected in unit time per unit current. In unit time heat energy in amount $iP_{\perp\parallel}$ flows into the box, energy is convected in by the current in amount $iU_{\perp}$, where $U_{\perp}$ is written because on the entrance side current flows perpendicular to the crystal axis, and energy $iU_{\parallel}$ is convected out. This is all there is; in particular there is no Poynting flow because there is no double layer and no potential jump in the surface. Equating the energy flowing out to that flowing in gives,

$$i(U_{\parallel} - U_{\perp}) = iP_{\perp\parallel} \quad \cdot \quad \cdot \quad \cdot \quad \cdot \quad (5)$$

The current cancels. We may replace the Peltier heat by an expression in the Thomson heats by the two fundamental relations (3) and (4), obtaining,

53

$$U_{\parallel} - U_{\perp} = \tau \int_0^{\tau} \frac{\sigma_{\parallel} - \sigma_{\perp}}{\tau} \, d\tau \qquad . \qquad . \qquad . \quad (6)$$

The lower limit of temperature integration is taken as 0° Absolute because of the third law of thermodynamics, which demands that Peltier and Thomson heats vanish at 0° Absolute. The solution of this equation for U is

$$U_{\alpha} = \tau \int_0^{\tau} \frac{\sigma_{\alpha}}{\tau} \, d\tau + f(\tau),$$

where the subscript α indicates that the expression is to be formed for either the parallel or perpendicular direction of flow. The temperature function of integration $f(\tau)$ is not a function of orientation. Since in an isothermal conductor steady flow of current is accompanied by no thermal effects (except Joulean heating), f must reduce to a constant, independent of temperature and dependent only on the substance. We have then finally,

$$U_{\alpha} = \tau \int_0^{\tau} \frac{\sigma_{\alpha}}{\tau} \, d\tau + \text{const (material)}. \qquad . \qquad . \quad (7)$$

Next consider an element of volume in the homogeneous conductor where current flows through a temperature gradient at constant orientation, as indicated in Figure 4. We suppose the conductor

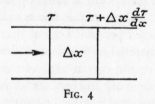

FIG. 4

lagged laterally, so that there is no entrance of heat by lateral conduction, and the only heat entering the element is by conduction along the axis in virtue of a longitudinal temperature gradient. Now there are several energy manifestations in this element of volume, and each of them demands its own verbal formulation. These different formulations should be consistent with each other, and if they correspond to anything more than mere conventions, should be capable of some sort of instrumental contact. There are at least four of these energy aspects : there is the total energy in all forms entering and leaving the region, there is the energy associated with the current, there is the total energy associated with the matter within the region, and there is energy in the form of heat associated with the matter.

Consider first the total energy. Since energy is not created we have to verbalise this as, 'total energy entering region is equal to total energy leaving region (for unit time), or *net* energy entering equals zero.' Energy gets into and out of the region in only three ways ; by convection by the current, by thermal conduction, and by flow on the Poynting vector through the lateral surface, where there is a Poynting vector normal to the surface. Writing in order the net energy of these three processes gives the equation

$$-\frac{d}{dx}(iU) + \frac{d}{dx}\left(\kappa\frac{d\tau}{dx}\right) - i\frac{dV}{dx} = 0. \qquad . \qquad . \quad (8)$$

Here κ is the longitudinal thermal conductivity and the subscript has been omitted from U since the orientation remains constant for these considerations and it is not necessary to specify it.

Next consider the energy associated with the current. I think we are under compulsion to verbalise this as follows, 'Excess energy carried out of the region over that carried in by the current is equal to the total energy acquired by the current within the region.' We already know how to write the excess energy convected out. The energy acquired by the current within the region consists of three parts. There is the energy acquired as Thomson heat. In this particular set-up in which there is lateral lagging to prevent lateral entrance of heat, the source of this Thomson heat energy must be described as the ' matter ' within the element. In an alternative set-up, in which there is no lateral lagging, but excess heat is fed in laterally when current flows so as to maintain the temperature *status quo*, we would say that the current extracted its Thomson heat from the lateral flow from the surroundings. There is also another type of interchange of energy between current and matter within the element, namely in the form of Joulean heat. Matter acquires Joulean heat, and the current loses an equal amount of energy. Finally, the source of the Poynting outflow from the region must be described as the current. The mechanism of this flow is by the current flowing through the potential gradient of the field. Writing out the explicit expressions for these three energy acquisitions by the current gives for the equation of energy balance on the current,

$$\frac{d}{dx}(iU) = i\sigma\frac{d\tau}{dx} - i^2r - i\frac{dV}{dx} \qquad . \qquad . \quad (9)$$

Here r is resistance per unit length.

55

We have now formulated our first two demands, with respect to total energy and energy associated with the current. Our next two demands were with regard to energy associated with the matter. Since the matter is in a steady state, there can be no change in the associated energy within the region, so that our two formulations become ; 'net energy associated with matter leaving region is equal to energy acquired by matter inside,' and ' net energy in the form of heat associated with matter leaving the region is equal to energy in form of heat acquired by matter inside.' These two demands here become identical, for the only energy associated with matter with which we are concerned is heat energy, since there is no motion of the parts and there are no elastic stresses, and there are no electrical forces acting on matter, so that there is no mechanical energy involved in any form. The heat associated with matter entering or leaving is conduction heat. Heat is acquired by the matter inside in two forms ; as Joulean heat from the current and as Thomson heat from the current (this is negative because this heat is imparted). The equation of energy balance on the matter is therefore,

$$- \kappa \frac{d^2\tau}{dx^2} = i^2 r - i\sigma \frac{d\tau}{dx} \quad . \quad \quad . \quad \quad . \quad . \ (10)$$

All the terms in this last equation have full instrumental significance, so that it is capable of direct experimental check. This check is met within experimental error.

In fact, in practice the equation is usually inverted and used as a means of determining σ, since temperature gradients are easier to measure than the small amounts of heat involved in a direct determination of the Thomson heat.

We must demand that our method of verbalising the different aspects be consistent. This is at once seen to be the case, because on eliminating U between equations (8) and (9) we obtain (10).

What account do we thus obtain of the detailed action in different parts of the circuit? It is obvious that the thermoelectric circuit involves ' non-field' forces, because otherwise current would not flow. How are these ' non-field' forces distributed ? The ' non-field' force is defined through Ohm's law by the equation

$$i = \text{total force}/r = (E_{n.f.} + E_f)/r,$$

where $E_{n.f.}$ is the ' non-field' force, and E_f is the ' field' force, given here by the negative gradient of the potential function. We may solve this equation for $E_{n.f.}$ obtaining $E_{n.f.} = ir - E_f = ir + \frac{dV}{dx}$.

We may substitute this expression at once in equation (9) obtaining,

$$\frac{dU}{dx} = \sigma \frac{d\tau}{dx} - E_{n.f.}$$

U is known and given by equation (7). Substituting for U and solving for $E_{n.f.}$ gives, after a simple reduction,

$$E_{n.f.} = -\frac{d\tau}{dx} \int_0^\tau \frac{\sigma}{\tau} d\tau \quad . \qquad . \qquad . \qquad . \quad (11)$$

This ' non-field ' force is located only in the body of the metal where there is a temperature gradient and does not occur at the junction between the two orientations. This is already implied in the fact that there is no electric double layer or jump in potential at the interface. The localisation of $E_{n.f.}$ is thus quite different from the localisation of the energy intakes by the current by means of which the current is maintained. For the energy intakes are, for normal substances, almost entirely situated at the interface, where the energy intake is equal to the Peltier heat. There is also an energy intake in the body of the metal equal to the Thomson heat, but this is in general smaller than the Peltier intake. These energy intakes, which as a whole maintain the current, are obviously closely related to what is called an electromotive force in simple situations, such as the battery already considered. Let us define a corresponding electromotive force in our thermocouple. The total electromotive force in the circuit is usually defined as the total energy delivered to the current by outside sources when unit quantity of electricity flows around the circuit. Here the outside source of energy is thermal and the total electromotive force is the total heat absorbed. The precise meaning of ' outside sources ' in this definition requires some elucidation. The Joulean heat generated by the current and imparted to the material of the conductor might, in a literal application of the definition, be taken as an ' outside source ' of energy (negative). However, this Joulean heat dissipated by the current is not regarded in the definition as part of the ' outside source ' but is treated as energy received from the source and dissipated through the agency of the current. Neither is the energy received in any element of the current by the Poynting vector understood in the definition as an ' outside source,' energy on the Poynting vector being a ' field ' energy, whereas the ' outside source ' is a ' non-field ' source.

The total electromotive force of the circuit, which may be referred to in the conventional way as total E.M.F., must be due to action in the parts of the circuit. It is one of the tasks of a complete theory of our system to find explicit expressions for this localised action. At the junctions there is an intake of heat energy, and consistently with the definition of E.M.F. for the complete circuit we localise in each junction an E.M.F. equal to the Peltier heat at the junction. Similarly in the body of the conductor where there is a temperature gradient there is a heat intake distributed along the length of the conductor, and equal per unit length of the conductor, to

$\sigma \dfrac{dx}{d\tau}$. We recognise, therefore, in the body of the conductor, a *distributed* electromotive force, which delivers so much energy per unit length (and per unit quantity of electricity). Since this source delivers energy per unit length, its dimensions are different from the total E.M.F. We may call this a 'distributed E.M.F.,' and denote it by e.m.f., the small letters calling attention to the difference in dimensions.[1] The dimensions of E.M.F. are the dimensions of e.m.f. times length. We have explicitly,

$$\text{e.m.f.} = \sigma \frac{d\tau}{dx}. \qquad . \qquad . \qquad . \qquad . \quad (12)$$

It is to be noticed that the e.m.f. in the body of the conductor is not equal to the $E_{n.f.}$ at the same point, but in general has a different sign. There is, however, a relation between e.m.f. and $E_{n.f.}$ for the complete circuit, for it is easy to show that $\oint \text{e.m.f.}\ ds = \oint E_{n.f.} ds$.

The detailed situation in a thermo-couple is thus completely different from the simple situation inside a battery, where elementary analysis shows that $E_{n.f.}$ is identically equal to the e.m.f. at all points within the battery and also at outside points. This has, I believe, been assumed to be the case in general. It certainly was the assumption made by Heaviside. It is evident that here we have something more general than is contemplated in the classical scheme of description of phenomena within massive conductors as exemplified in the field equations. What was not contemplated in the classical scheme was that the current might receive 'non-field' energy in one locality and transport it and dump it in another. This is shown by the equation obtained from (11) and (12)

[1] In my book *The Thermodynamics of Electrical Phenomena in Metals*, New York, 1934, a different notation was used for these two quantities. What is here called $E_{n.f.}$ was there called (e.m.f.)$_d$ ('Driving electro-motive force') and what is here called e.m.f. was there called (e.m.f.)$_w$ ('Working electro-motive force').

$$\text{e.m.f.} - E_{n.f.} = \frac{dU}{dx} \qquad . \qquad . \qquad . \qquad . \qquad (13)$$

There was no place for such an energy in the classical scheme, the only (recognised) energy of the current being the field energy, the transformations of which were described by the Poynting vector. With recognition of the electron character of an electric current a place became apparent for such a non-field energy in the kinetic energy of the electrons, and a sufficiently acute realisation of the consequences of this might have led to a re-examination of the classical fundamentals.

The total energy, U, convected by the current contains, according to equation (7), a constant of the material. Subtracting off this constant, it is natural to describe the part $\tau \int_0^\tau \frac{\sigma}{\tau} d\tau$ as 'thermal energy,' since thermal energy enters the system in this amount. Denote this by U_τ, where

$$U_\tau = \int_0^\tau \frac{\sigma}{\tau} d\tau \qquad . \qquad . \qquad . \qquad (14)$$

Let us examine further the consequences of 'saying' that this energy convected by the current is 'thermal' energy. Any reversible transformations of this energy within the system should be subject to the second law of thermodynamics. In the body of the metal there is a temperature gradient and a reversible Thomson heat and the second law should have something to say. Apply the second law to the volume element of Figure 4. The fraction $\Delta\tau/\tau$ of the heat convected into the region by the current at the higher temperature should be reversibly transformed within the region. Comparison shows that this is exactly the amount calculated above which is converted. The point of view is thus checked.

To give the final touch of confirmation to the consistency of this point of view, it should be possible to associate an entropy flow with the current. Consistency with the point of view of the first lecture would then demand that there be a connection between the net entropy flux out of any region and the creation of entropy by irreversible processes within the region. If U is properly described as 'thermal energy,' then we must 'say' that the current i convects with it the entropy Ui/τ or $i\int\frac{\sigma}{\tau} d\tau$. Consider now the element of volume of

Figure 4. There are two entropy fluxes, that of the electric current above, and that due to thermal conduction and equal to $\vec{q}/\tau$, where $\vec{q}$ is the thermal current, here equal to $-\kappa\dfrac{d\tau}{dx}$. The net entropy leaving due to the flux per unit length is (d/dx) (Flux). Inside unit length two irreversible processes occur which create entropy. Joulean heating, which creates entropy at the rate $i^2 r/\tau$, and thermal conduction, which in general creates entropy at the rate $\vec{q}$. grad τ/τ^2, which here is equal to $\kappa\,(d\tau/dx)^2/\tau^2$. We then have the equation,

$$\frac{d}{dx}\left[i\int_0^\tau \frac{\sigma}{\tau}\,d\tau - \frac{\kappa}{\tau}\frac{d\tau}{dx}\right] = \frac{i^2 r}{\tau} + \frac{\kappa}{\tau^2}\left(\frac{d\tau}{dx}\right)^2.$$

Reference to equations (8), (9) and (10) shows that this condition is identically satisfied.

Our verbal demands have therefore led to a completely consistent paper-and-pencil scheme. Furthermore, most of the constructions of our paper-and-pencil scheme, such as $E_{n.f.}$, e.m.f., and U_τ, make direct and unique instrumental contact. This is highly gratifying and suggests, perhaps, that we might hope to find the counterparts of these things if we could extend our theory so as to give a detailed mechanism for them. This has indeed been done by Houston,[1] who has worked out the electron theory of thermoelectricity, and found the specific electron mechanism responsible for each of these three things, $E_{n.f.}$, e.m.f., and U_τ.

Finally, it remains only to drop the restriction to single crystals which has applied to our discussions since page 150. If we carry over our scheme without alteration, using all the same letters and the same formulas, with merely the addition of a subscript to the various pertinent quantities, such as P or σ or U_τ, to denote the particular metal we are dealing with, we shall obviously still have an internally consistent scheme, which satisfies all our verbal demands and the laws of thermodynamics. In particular this will mean that in the general case of two different metals there is no potential jump at the interface corresponding to the Peltier heat, contrary to Heaviside. If the argument is re-examined it will be seen that this is basic to the whole treatment, and that without it our new constructional quantities could not have been made to fit into an edifice consistent with each other and thermodynamics. There is only one essential difference between two different metals and two orientations of the same crystal, namely

[1] W. V. Houston, *Journal of Applied Physis*, 1941, **12**, 519-529

that in the expression for the total energy convected by the current as given by equation (7), a constant of the material now appears which may be different for two different metals. This means that when a current flows across an interface there must be an energy influx to provide for the difference of U due to the two different metals, and this energy influx *is not thermal*. The only other possible source of energy influx is on the Poynting vector, which did not exist at the junction for two orientations of the same metal. This means that in the case of two different metals we must recognise the possibility of a double layer at the interface and a corresponding jump of potential. However, there is no thermal involvement of this double layer or its forces. We are here concerned with an aspect of the Volta effect, which we have already seen involves a possible double layer on any of three surfaces, subject to only a single condition, making it impossible to uniquely fix the potential jump at any face and in particular at the interface between the metals. This will remain as an essential indetermination until new types of experimental effects are discovered and taken into consideration. Until then, surface double layers and potential jumps do not have full instrumental status but retain some of the character of pure constructions.

In conclusion, in this lecture we have seen how our paper-and-pencil manipulations and verbal demands have led to constructions to which, in most cases, we have eventually been able to give complete instrumental status. I think this is characteristic of most scientific enterprise. We employ our instrumental and our paper-and-pencil and verbal operations together in a way to mutually reinforce and supplement each other. In this way new insights into the experimental domain may be indicated which may later be verified by the experiments thus suggested. In fact the two sorts of operations are so closely intertwined that it seems impossible to separate them sharply and indeed it would probably be meaningless to attempt to do so.

INDEX

A
Action at a distance, 14ff
Awareness, 7

B
Biological systems, 41
Boiler pressure, 45
Boltzmann, 40
Brownian motion, 22

C
Calorimetry, 32
Conduction of heat, entropy
  associated with, 37, 38
Conservation, 32
Conventions, 24, 25
Correlation, 17
Creation of entropy, 36
Crises for the energy
  concept, 25
Crystals, thermo-electric
  phenomena in, 55ff
Current vector, 44

D
DeDonder, 40
Differential equations as
  requiring verification, 13
Distributed electromotive
  force, 58
Double layer, 46

E
Eckart, 40
Einstein, 14, 26
Electromotive force, 48
Electron emission, 47
Emergence into instrumental
  operations, 10

Empty space, 18, 19
Energy, convected by electric
  current, 53ff
  localization, 29ff
  as tensor, 29
Entropy 34ff
  convected by electric
  current, 59, 60
Experiments, mental, 9
  verbal, 9
Extended entropy, 42

F
Falling body, 12
Faraday, 14, 44
Field concept, 14ff
Fine, 40
First law of thermo-
  dynamics, 23ff
Flux, of energy, 27, 33
  of entropy, 35
  of heat, 27
  of mechanical energy
  (work), 27
Force on electricity, 44
Free invention, 9

H
Heat conduction, 28
Heat transport by
  radiation, 28
Heaviside, 46, 50, 58
Houston, 60

I
Irreversible processes, 36ff

J
Joulean heating, entropy

associated with, 38, 39

K

Kelvin, 39, 46, 49

L

Light, as thing travelling, 20ff
Limiting process, 15, 16
Localization of energy, 29ff
  of entropy, 35
Logic, 11
Lorentz, 9

M

Mass-energy relation, 26
Mathematics, 10ff
Maxwell, 14, 43, 46
Mechanism of field action, 16
von Mises plasticity
  criterion, 42

N

Natural law, 34
"Non-field" force, 45, 50, 56
Non-thermal convected
  energy, 61

O

Operational analysis, 7
Operations, instrumental, 8
  "paper-and-pencil", 8, 9
  verbal, 9,
Ostwald, 22

P

Peltier heat, 48ff

Photons, 20, 21
Plastic body, 41-42
Poincaré, 24
Potential jumps, 46, 47
Poynting vector, 30, 47
Prigogine, 40
Propagation, 21

R

Radiant heat, 34
Reality, 10, 22, 27
Reification of energy, 26
Van Rysselberghe, 40

S

State couples, 26
  of system, 24

T

Thermodynamics, 23ff
Thermo-electric circuit, 39
  power, 48
Thomson heat, 49ff
Thomson, J. J., 18
Tolman, 40

V

Verication, 12
Velocity of light, 20
Volta effect, 45ff

W

Wilson condensation
  chamber, 22

Z

Zero point field, 19